A Survivor of Love

The author

Soonita Rockett

A Survivor of Love

Olympia Publishers
London

www.olympiapublishers.com
OLYMPIA PAPERBACK EDITION

A CIP catalogue record for this title is
available from the British Library.

ISBN: 978-1-84897-625-2

(Olympia Publishers is part of Ashwell Publishing Ltd)

This is a work of fiction.
Names, characters, places and incidents originate from the writer's
imagination. Any resemblance to actual persons, living or dead, is purely
coincidental.

First Published in 2015

Olympia Publishers
60 Cannon Street
London
EC4N 6NP

Printed in Great Britain

In dedication to my Granny who looks after my babies in the world of spirit and for all continuing to love and support me through life. I love you xxx

Acknowledgements

A heartfelt acknowledgement to Nicola Farmer who helped me to believe in myself and trust my gift. Meeting Nicola opened up new doors for me aiding my excelled journey to healing in the arms of the angels. She is also a lady that communicates with the angels and confirmed my supernatural experiences in the early days, bringing me comfort. Thank you, lady of the heart.

To my husband who continues to walk this path with me through the hard times and the good. Thank you for staying by my side, for sharing this life with me and forever loving me. I love you with all my heart.

I thank God for blessing me with the most beautiful girl in the world! My daughter, Anisha. She is my rock and inspiration. She keeps me sane and forever strong. I live for you sweetheart... my world.

My daddy has always been an amazing support. He taught me how to be a doting loving parent and how to love. I thank you, Daddy, for everything you have ever done for me and for still loving me just as much today as you did the day I was born. I couldn't have asked for a better father. I am blessed.

I acknowledge my lovely mum who, despite her own traumas and strife, has done all she can for me and helped to make this book possible. Thank you, Mummy! With love always.

My pets are an important part of my family and I love them all so dearly. Thank you for all the comfort you bring me during my intervals of relaxation and for making me smile every day. Rocky, Princess, Shyla, Isis and Gizmo... my loves.

Thank you to Olympia Publishers who not only considered my story, but have given tremendous support and acted wonderfully on my behalf. I am forever thankful to the angels for guiding me in your direction.

Finally... I thank all the amazing people that have been a part of my life up until now, bringing me to this point that I am so grateful for. I am so very blessed with many beautiful souls that surround me on the Earth and I love each and every one of you.

Introduction

A Pre-Note

As you read the contents of my book, I want you to release all your previous learnings, any stigma's from society, all that you have learnt to be only fairy tales and everything that different religions have ever taught you to believe. As you read through the pages, please read as though you are a blank slate, with no judgement or limitations to what is possible. I am sure for most readers this book will hit on something quite impossible to believe. But what if I told you that nothing was impossible. Life itself holds no limits to potential, the only limitations are the ones you place upon yourself. How incredible might the world be? And now I welcome you, with love, into my world.

As with every journey of the human soul on Earth, my life has had its hardship, its laughter, sadness and most fortunately... love. I was born as a blank slate, like every other human being, allowing life itself to imprint upon me. To teach me and guide me. We are all one light. Within that light that we are as one, we hold many filaments waiting to be activated. As we achieve another goal, another test set upon our soul journey, another filament is activated. One filament may hold a lesson of giving of yourself, another might be an act of kindness, and another might be self-drive/motivation, another unconditional love and so on. The more filaments that you activate the higher your potential becomes, therefore the more you empower yourself, and the brighter your own soul light shines.

In my teaching practices, I have many pupils who come to me wanting to develop their mediumship abilities. Some desperately wanting to communicate with spirit, so that they may share this wonderful gift to light up the lives of others. My dear friends, Mediumship is merely the very tip of the iceberg to your potential. Your potential of your own abilities, the potential to all you wish to gain and all you wish to give. Your own potential is limitless. The mission for every soul upon this Earth, is to master the self. Once you have mastered this, your journey is complete. You are in a position to give effortlessly, to give wisely and to share your own wisdoms with your peers, in beginning their own journeys.

It is most important for all the readers of my journey to know, that I don't hold any religious beliefs and do not class myself to fall under any title of religion. I simply AM. Everything I speak to you about in this book are my own personal experiences. Some of these experiences you will read are shared with those snatched from different religions. If I happen to mention certain figures that you are aware of from the Bible, please know that I speak in only truth of my experience shared with that figure. Some may shy away from the mention of Jesus, however I refer to Jesus only as a wonderful being of love and light and one of the most inspirational teachers of our history. The fact is that people like Jesus, Moses and Peter etc were historical figures who played big roles in shaping society at that time. Reports of other figures of our known history, such as Julius Ceaser and King Henry VIII, are no different to the religious figures mentioned.

Many of the teachings I receive from higher realms come from many historically known figures such as, ancient pharaohs, gods and goddesses (Who all once walked the Earth, but are worshipped as gods), Native American leaders, Mother Theresa, Ghandi etc. These are all figures which once came to the Earth and helped to form society, by teaching massive lessons on the most important energy... LOVE. These wonderful teachers of our history still reside amongst the energies, waiting upon our callings to further teach those who are willing to listen, those who are willing to learn. That energy I speak of that we reside with, is the universe. We are all but a speckle within that one big energy. We are all a part of that bigger picture. We all hold the ability to channel into every aspect of that big picture, the universe.

This now takes me onto other energies that may be difficult for some readers to understand alongside their current understandings/beliefs. Extra-terrestrial life forms and beings, though only mentioned on a small scale within the journey I share with you here, they are never the less mentioned. But as I speak of all being but a speckle within the Universe which is infinity, then surely we are not the only life forms of the universe? And if we have the ability to tap into other energies of the universe, then of course we can communicate with these beings also.

Many theorists, scientist and religious cults try to take ownership of different aspects of the universe. Aspects that have influenced Earthly life and civilisations in history. Religion will speak of God and the creator. Science will speak of the Big Bang theories and evolution. Ancient Alien Theorists will argue that all of our progression in life is solely down to Alien encounters and how they came to teach us their ways and help us move forwards in life. Most people are drawn to at least one of these theories to explain our existence to which we live now. Actually instead of embracing just one of these aspects to explain everything, why can't it be all three? Why are we afraid to expand our acceptance and learning to the Truth. The Truth which is all. Everything as one.

And now I speak of the Truth. That oneness. That highest and most powerful Love energy, this is the energy that has gathered much confusion over all of our earthly existences in time and beyond. Yet it is the energy that is the purest of them all. This is the energy many religions have named, God. My beautiful friends of the light, God is merely a name, which has been given to this wonderful energy. So if you have trouble swallowing the Truth of this energy? This energy that has at times been tainted by the teachings of different religions and understandings, then simply re- name it. It is the creator of all existence and all that we know. Is it not the act of making love that creates another being, another life to this Earth? Is it not the energy of love that conquers all others? These are the truths and this energy is the creator. This energy is Love. When I speak of this energy in my book, I refer to the source as, God. This is by choice and not by religious influence. So let's start from the beginning, as I invite you into my life and to travel my journey so far. I hope you find it as fascinating as I have and that it shifts your awareness closer to the Truth, closer to the source of life and the potential that love carries... infinity.

Chapter 1

My Story

I didn't become aware of my ability to communicate, converse with and see spirit until the age of twenty-nine. However, my dealings with spirits went back *way* further than that! Now I understand, I'm not afraid, I understand that they are just people on a higher ground than us, people who have reached that next stage in life. I also have trust in my loving and loyal spirit guide, Mary, that she protects me from any spirit that might want to cause upset or harm to me. So I have no reason to be scared. Like I said though... this understanding didn't come till the age of twenty-nine!

From as little as the age of two years old I have memories of screaming, being scared and frightened that someone else, or something else was in my bedroom with me. I have always doted on by my daddy and always been a daddy's girl, so of course I wanted to spend every second with him. But that wasn't the only reason I insisted on sleeping in Mummy's and Daddy's bed, every single night. My bedroom was only next to theirs and even angled so I could see into their room from my bed... But that wasn't good enough. I needed to be close to them for protection. Protection from what? I don't know. I just knew there was always other people around me that no one could see. Things got so bad my parents ended up putting up a bed in their room, right at the end of theirs for me to sleep. But it was my daddy that ended up sleeping in that, bless him, as I just couldn't be alone. Mum was never too happy about that... But Daddy always gave into me.

We moved to another house when I was aged four years old and even though my bedroom joined onto my parents, I would again spend most nights in the bed with them. I don't remember my brothers ever being like this, except when they were ill. I would wish I was brave and could be a big girl sleeping alone in her own bedroom, but as often as I would try, they would make themselves known to me. They were there, watching, maybe trying to talk. I think I was just so scared I blocked it out as much as I could. I would still see little balls of lights floating around and shadows on the wall. I would see people in my mind's eye... many different people over the years, though would just be told it was my imagination.

I only began sleeping in my own room all night once my little brother came along. I was told it was my job to look after him at night. We shared a bedroom and I did feel very grown up, being the big, responsible sister... however there were still times that it all got too much and I would end up abandoning him and climbing into bed with Mummy and Daddy. It would always be Daddy I went to... Mum was a heavy sleeper and even when I did manage to wake her, she was much less sympathetic than Dad. Daddy always had a little deeper understanding and ability to give himself more (emotionally). They were just raised differently, I think. My father was Mauritian and his family descended from India. They were very doted on as children, the mother was always affectionate, loving and concerning. The children always came first! And that is how my father was... most of the time... My mother came from a very traditional English, Yorkshire family.

My granddad seamed the more affectionate out of my grandparents, on my mum's side. He worked away a lot. My grandma, as lovely as she is, was always known for being very strict with children... She used to scare me when I was little, I tell you! My mother was the oldest of five girls and there wasn't that many years between them. So you can understand Grandma being rather stressed and relying on my mother to help out allot with the younger ones... One thing I did learn from my mother's side of the family and in my mother's ways.... Children certainly did not come first! People just have different views I guess... I always preferred my daddy's ways though.

Lots of children have imaginary friends and I was no exception. The only thing was that my imaginary friends were very much real. They were my bestest friends... They never judged me, argued with me and were never mean. I had three of them and they would always be together. I named them myself as I didn't know their names, but they didn't mind. They would even chat away back to me ... and I know for sure that wasn't my imagination. Like when they would advise me against doing something for my own safety, or tell me what was going on inside the house, whilst we were playing outside. I didn't think anything of it then and strangely... I wasn't ever frightened of these three girls. One wore a Victorian outfit and I would always comment on her lovely dress and white hat. Another wore pretty, frilly dresses. These two girls were white with blond hair. The third had darker skin and dark hair and wore tattier, normal clothes. She reminded me of *me*, so I named her Soonita. I didn't know their real names so I named them myself.

The girl in the pretty dresses I named Jamyma and the Victorian girl, Joanne. If I was on the swing they would be all stood around me and we would chat away together. It was one of those girls that showed me that the bars on the swing could be used to play and sit on as well... Just as she did when I was on the swing. I always got into trouble for that. I would say, "Well Jamyma does it! And she doesn't fall off!" When I was on the climbing frame, they would climb up with me, except one of the girls. She didn't like the climbing frame, but was happy to stand at the bottom and watch. I would try to encourage her and tell her it was alright. She was the very sensible one out of the three. This was the Victorian girl, Joanne. She would forewarn me when I was about to have an accident, telling me the consequences of what could happen if I were to carry on. Stuff rather advanced for my mind at that age. At the age of five and six years I was nowhere near as clever as kids today at that age! I would just tell her (knowing better of course) that I would be alright and carried on anyway... She was always right of course... However, after, she would never gloat or say "I told you so" She would just comfort me and tell me to go tell Mummy or Daddy. She would even help me up when I was really hurt.

One time I was playing out in the garden on my bike. Before we had the extension built there was a garage and pebbly bit of path going down the side of the house. I would take the bike down that bit, even though it was tight. I was still only just learning to ride without stabilisers, so would often topple off. This particular time I don't know what happened! I fell off so lopsided, down the side of the house that when I looked down at my leg, it was all tangled in the chains and tucked into the spokes of the bike. I was in a lot of pain, though was more panicked that I didn't have a clue how I was to get out! And because of where I fell Daddy couldn't see me from the house and most likely wouldn't hear my screams. I just lay on the floor for a little while becoming more and more panicked and upset. Every time I would try to drag my leg back through the tangled chain it would tighten and cut into my ankle. I didn't know what to do, then suddenly the bike moved.... Everything just seemed to open up and I was able to slide out my foot and ankle with no effort. I managed to get myself up and said "Thank you!" I don't know who to as I couldn't see anyone there, only my Victorian friend who helped me up and walked me into the house with her arm around me as I sobbed feeling sorry for myself. Can you believe after all that I had just a graze on my elbow and cut on my leg? It was a pretty nasty cut though and really hurt! I still have the scar on my knee now, from that day. I was about six years old then. As I sobbed and told Daddy what had happened, I told him my friends helped me.

He told me off, saying I was getting too old now to have imaginary friends and that I should stop.

I learnt to keep my friends to myself a lot. I would reassure them that they didn't have to feel hurt from what others said about them, because I knew they were real. This was always more my concern though, as they didn't seem fazed. They would look sorry at times however, if I'd just been told off for mentioning them. As I got older our playtime together became less and less, but they were still with me. We talked more and more, but I started to see them less and less. Always instinctively knowing they were there though and always hearing their voices chime back to me in conversation. My mum and dad were very busy, running businesses and I was just left to entertain myself much of the time. We just chatted about general stuff mainly. When I was upset, or down they would offer words of reassurance and help me pull myself together, giving me ideas to be getting on with next.

I recently found out my mother had a miscarriage one year after giving birth to me. When I think back to how alike one of my "imaginary friends" looked like me... So much so, I named her the same name as me... I wonder if this was my sister who died in my mother's womb. Babies and children who pass away still progress in the spirit world. They grow up in heaven, just as we do on earth. As older children and adults, they look as they would have on the earth. There would not have been one full year between myself and my sister, which is most likely why she appeared to look so like me and the same age. I know this as not only do I have my own spirit children in heaven, but I have seen other people's children in the heavens too. For example, I gave a reading to one lady. I described a boy that came through with two aunties by his side. I described the boy and said he looked about seventeen years old. The lady whom I was giving a reading thought about this for a moment. "I did lose a nephew..." She said. "And he did have blonde hair and blue eyes as you said and would always have a side parting..." She carried on. "But he died very young. He was only three years old." I asked her how long ago did her nephew pass away and she replied that it was well over ten years ago. "In fact..." She thought again for a moment, trying to work out her maths. "He would be seventeen years old now!" Well that explained it. "So they grow up on the other side do they?" I explained this phenomena to her a little and gave some other examples to confirm this to her. "Well... I know the other two ladies are definitely my aunties from how you describe them. It's nice to hear that they have looked after him all that time. *They* must have raised him in heaven. I'm really pleased about that, because they were the best aunties and so lovely."

When I was nine years old I remember being in the car with my mum and younger brother and for some reason mentioned my friends again. My mum looked at me through her rear-view mirror with a surprised and confused look on her face. "Do you still talk to them then?" she said. I told her that they've always been my friends and had never left me and that they still played with me at times too. She told me that day, very calm and nicely that I should stop talking too them now as I was getting to old to have them as my friends. Weirdly... even though I know she was still thinking them to be my imaginary friends (which I even lead myself to believe and referred to them as so, as that's what everyone else would say they were whenever I talked about them), I knew she was right. I thought about this a lot over the next couple of days, feeling very sad to say goodbye to them. But I did. I told them that I couldn't play with them anymore and thanked them for being my friends over the years. They were lovely about it and seemed to completely understand and not be offended. They told me how they have enjoyed our time together and bought lots of lovely memories into my mind of times that we had played our games. They told me that they loved me very much and would never forget me and I told them I felt the same... Suddenly, they were gone... There was a feeling of emptiness inside me and the warm tingle I would feel inside whenever they were around me... Was now gone. I cried as I was so sad, but couldn't tell anyone about it, because I knew they wouldn't understand.

Even at the age of eleven I remember sitting in my bedroom, thinking about them. I missed more than anything just having someone to talk to when I felt down, confused, angry or upset. They were always there for me, no matter what trouble I got myself into. One day I lay on my bed feeling lonely, bored and upset about something, wishing my friends were with me to talk to... and I heard a voice in my mind say "You can talk to me." The voice told me that I could tell him anything in my prayers and he would always help me when possible. From this time on that is exactly what I would do... I speak to God.

I didn't come from an overly religious family. I wasn't one of these kids where religion and wise teachings from the bible were impressed on me. I found my own way in life and had my own very personal relationship with God. I did really enjoy the bible stories, retold to us in our school assemblies, however. Whether true or not, I learned so much from them. My morals mainly and how to treat others with thought and care. You wouldn't of known that when I got to my teens though! I was somewhat of a troubled tearaway teen... but I'll get to that bit, later.

Chapter 2

My Gentleman's Protection

I was about eleven years old and there was a big change around in our house. I had now been given a much bigger bedroom, which I loved! I had Daddy's old Hi-Fi and big speakers, a massive set of wardrobes with big mirrors going all along and a sofa bed for when friends would come to visit (a sofa bed as well as my bed). I loved most that I was now in one of the bedrooms at the front of the house, because now I could see my tree. It wasn't really my tree. It was a massive oak tree that had always been on the opposite side of the road from my house. I used to be fascinated by that tree and whenever I felt down I would just stare at that tree and it's as if it gave me an inner strength. Strength I most certainly needed when I was a bit older! When I was young I would stare at that tree from our big bay windows in the living room. That tree could look so different depending on the season. But to me, it was always beautiful. Especially on wet windy days I would love just sitting inside in the warm house, watching that tree.

My bed went alongside the big windows and at night I would fall to sleep staring at the stars and my big tree. It offered some comfort and helped me relax, because even now, I felt watched. It was very brave of me to accept that bedroom. The main reason being that having that room, meant I was all alone in that whole section of the house... In fact I was all alone in the whole upstairs of the house!! It was a very big house. But I loved the room so much and I thought now really should be my time that I start growing up and showing everyone just how brave I was.

I'd started having lots of dreams at this point that would end up coming true. Just little silly situations. Moments that most people would refer to as "Deja vu." Only my moments were actually moments that I had dreamt and I would remember the dreams quite clearly as the moment would unfold in line with the order of my dream from previous weeks before. I have come to learn now that this is a form of precognition. A form of predicting or seeing the future. I had been in my new bedroom for a few weeks, when one night I laid there and could hear some scuffling of feet out in the corridor. I knew no one had come up the stairs as I would normally hear the creaks or some footsteps. I felt uneasy and a little scared, but managed to stay in my room and fall asleep anyway. I always kept the hall light on, just in case I needed to get up for the toilet in the night. I also had a lamp kept on in my room through the night as I've always been afraid of the dark. I would keep the bedroom door half open, just in case I needed to shout to Daddy for anything. I woke in the night to see a man, very executive looking, like out of a fifties film with the hat and long coat. He just stood leaning round the door with a smile, then tipped his hat and bowed his head to me to say hello. He then went back into the hallway and walked down the corridor, but I didn't feel he was gone. He was still out in the corridor.

I felt as though I had seen this man before, but at the same time was quite freaked out by what had just happened. I couldn't go out the room to run down to Daddy as I knew the man was still out there, so I just screamed for him. I had to scream a few times and very loudly to be heard as his room was so far away. Sure enough though, he came running up to my screams. He wasn't one of these people that would hear you upset or scared and just stand at the bottom of the stairs shouting "what's the matter?" He would be by your side like lightening to respond to you and comfort you... That's just how I am now with my little girl, as it's something I appreciated so much of my own daddy when I was little. I told him what I had seen and he just tried to console and reassure me that it was just a bad dream. I knew it wasn't though. You can guess where I ended up sleeping that night. My poor mum and dad.

The next night I lay in my bed, trying to overcome my nerves, thinking of the events of the night before. Suddenly it came to me! A dream I'd had some months before. Not only had I dreamt the exact lay out of my bedroom, long before anyone knew I would have this room... I'd dreamt of the gentleman visitor from the night before. In my dream it was a repetitive cycle of me going to bed and laying down to sleep and as I did the gentleman would pop his head round the door to wish me a good night, then tell me he would be out in the hallway keeping watch and making sure I was safe. In my dream I wasn't scared. I just thanked him and said good night, as if I knew what he was on about and feeling rather grateful. As the dream went on I would see myself sleeping and the gentleman pacing up and down the corridor, every now and then popping his head around the door to make sure I was alright. Remembering the dream gave me some comfort that night, though I couldn't help wondering what he was protecting me from.

The next day I told my mother about the dream I had remembered and that I wasn't scared of the man anymore. She looked a little concerned however. That night she came home from work and had bought me a beautiful wooden cross with a silver Jesus Christ on it. She told me to hang it above my bed and nothing bad could ever come near me. I told her that I think that man was already doing this for me, but she said to do it anyway to be safe. She put a nail in the wall that very night and hung the cross above my bed. I really admired the beauty of that cross, though I'm not sure I fully believed it held any power to protect me. Not at that time in my life anyway. I just went along with it to keep Mum happy, which wasn't a regular occurrence.

As the nights went on I would hear the shuffling of feet out in the hallway. I would sometimes hear a sigh, or a cough. I began closing the door to my bedroom as I still felt uneasy to see the man again, however I would see his feet pass under the crack of the door, wearing his smart, black shoes. Sometimes, the bedroom door would even open itself slightly ajar, though I think the man knew I was a little scared to see him again (not that he was terrible to look at) so I would just see a shadow of a man spread across my wall, stay there for a moment, then go back out, the door closing behind him. I never would close the door completely however, so when the man was leaving my room again, I would ask in my mind not to close the door properly. When the door stopped in its correct position that I wanted, I would then thank him in my mind. For some reason though, there were still occasional nights that this was a bit much for me and I would become overwhelmed with fear and end up creeping back into Mum and Dad's bed. I suppose it was what they call "fear of the unknown."

Chapter 3

Granny xx

My daddy's sister, Aunty Soobeeta, was getting married. The most exciting part about this news was the fact my granny Algoo was going be coming from Mauritius to see her daughter marry. At nine years old I had no memories of my granny. I had only ever seen my granny as a baby, when we hadholiday's in Mauritius (as that is where my father is from), but of course I was too young to remember this. For some reason this time felt special! And I was so excited to meet her. I insisted on going to the airport with Mum and Dad to pick her up and bring her home. We all stood waiting at the arrivals area, next to the barrier. As I watched in anticipation and eagerness, my mum and dad joked that I was stood there watching for her arrival and I didn't even know what she looked like! "I do!" I told them. I said that she would have long, grey hair back in a plait, that she was short and that she would be wearing a red sari. My dad thought for a moment and said that I might be right and that she may well have grey hair by now. Mum just giggled and looked on.

I was the first one to spot Granny walk through the arrivals tunnel and I shouted and pointed straight away. Everyone looked over. My father came over all emotional at the sight of her, as he hadn't seen her for so many years. My mother just looked at me in shock, as Granny walked out exactly as I'd described her. I remember her asking how I knew, to which I replied "I don't know, I just knew." Unfortunately though, it wasn't the only thing I saw. At first when Granny walked through and down the arrivals corridor to get to us, I was excited to see her. But before she even got to us I asked "What's wrong with Granny? She's not well." She looked perfectly fine and my mum said just that. Dad even said she's fine. To look at her you wouldn't have thought anything, even after a thirteen hour flight! But something told me otherwise and I just knew she wasn't well. I don't know what I saw, or how I knew. We all slowly began walking towards a cafe further down the corridor and Daddy and Granny were just having general chit chat at first, but I kept running up to them to get Daddy's attention. "What's wrong with Granny? " I kept asking "What's wrong with Granny? She's not well."

Mum kept telling me off and saying to just give them a moment as they hadn't seen each other for so long. She also kept telling me that Granny was fine, but I was having none of it! Again I forcefully interrupted my dad and granny speaking to ask what was wrong with her. I was incredibly frustrated by this time and it was showing. Finally Daddy asked Granny if she was alright. I think it was something in the way Granny told Dad she was OK, as for some reason I saw him look a bit concerned as he asked her again. This time she told him she hadn't been well, but didn't want to tell him there and then what the problem was. Mum pulled me out the way at this point to help get the drinks.

When we came to sit back down, Daddy looked so worried and as if he'd been crying. Then for the first time ever, I heard the word... cancer. I listened to the conversations taking place around the table as action plans were being made. "I've told her," I said Daddy to Mum, "She's not leaving this country until it's sorted! This is the best country to be in to get the treatment she needs. She'll die if she goes back to Mauritius." My granny told my dad that she had not long found out before coming to England, that she had cancer. My dad, being a highly trained nurse, knew exactly how serious this was and what it would entail. Twenty years ago people still died of cancer, but it wasn't as common or as talked about as it is now. I was soon to learn all about it too.

My auntie's wedding came and went and the excitement of it all soon settled. Then Granny came to stay with us. I was so happy about this. She shared my bedroom. Her bed was by the window and mine on the other side of the room, so they made an L-shape. I was mesmerised by my granny. She had such long beautiful hair that she styled perfectly into a bun or plait, so effortlessly. She didn't even need a mirror or hair bobbles! She wore beautiful sari's that looked complicated to put on, but again she managed with little effort to dress. Every morning she would wake about six o'clock in the morning to dress, get a wash and do her hair. Once she was already, she would lay on top of her made bed and rest again for a few more hours... looking perfect. She was so dignified and had a real grace about her.

My granny couldn't speak a word of English and I couldn't speak her language. This didn't stop the special bond grow between us though. We could just sit and stare at each other for ages. I understood odd words and gestures she would make to me. One day I'd been playing downstairs and needed something from my bedroom. I went running up with the intention to come straight back down, to carry on my game. When I went into the room I saw Granny lying on the bed resting with the lights off. I got my toy and went to turn back out the room, when Granny called my name..."Vyervyer!" she said to me... Which meant come here. I went over to her. She nudged up on the bed and repeated herself gesturing for me to come sit by her, so I did. "Dormi" she said... Which meant sleep... I understood she was asking me to come lie with her a little while. She had her arm around me. With the other arm she moved the curtain a little and nodded towards the moon smiling. I knew she was telling me how beautiful the moon was. I sat up and opened the curtains properly, then laid back down with Granny. We laid for so long, just staring up at the clear starry sky and the full bright moon. We both fell asleep for a little while. I woke remembering my game I was playing earlier. I left Granny sleeping peacefully, sneaking out so not to disturb her.

I went through a time of getting really bad cramps in my calf muscles and aches. Growing pains my dad used to call them. I'd been laid on the sofa moaning and winging about it, so Dad came to try and soothe me with a massage. I was getting frustrated with him because he was squeezing too hard and was hurting me more. Bless him... He would try. Eventually I went upstairs in a huff, where Granny stood on top of the landing, about to come down, herself. As I'd said before, our house was very big. Daddy had been downstairs with me the whole time I'd been moaning about my painful leg, so Granny could not have known about my troubles... But somehow, she did... As poorly, weak and in pain as she was, she stopped me as I was about to reach the top of the stairs. She kneeled down onto her knees, put her hands around my painful lower leg and began massaging. How could she have known? And what's more is she went straight to the leg that was hurting, no hesitation. I felt terrible seeing her do this for me, especially when she was so poorly... I kept begging her to stop but she refused for at least two minutes before I could get her to stand back up. Strangely though... I clearly remember being very surprised as I laid on my bed, reading my book... The pain in my leg had completely gone.

Granny began deteriorating fast. She was in and out of hospital. When she got really bad and had to stay in hospital for a little while, Daddy would cook her fresh food every day and take it to her. She wasn't used to the English food and wasn't too keen. Daddy would make all her favourite foods, just how she liked, in attempts to encourage her to eat. She could only eat very little, if any. I remember going with Daddy a few times to visit Granny in hospital. I would always end up getting told off for something and Granny would tell Daddy off for doing so... She would speak in her language of course, but I understood... "Leave her, she's all right." She would say.

Granny had been back at home for a little while, when I suddenly became really worried about her. I had been sat in the bedroom with her (as I often would) and just thought she seemed in a bit more pain than usual. I kissed her on the cheek to offer some reassurance and let her know I loved her and she winced, as if in pain. I knew something wasn't right, so I went running downstairs to Daddy, urging him to go to her. He went up and sat with her a little while and noticed bruising all over her. Just to touch her lightly, she hurt and would bruise immediately. He called out the doctor (who would come to visit her often) and he called for an ambulance straight away and got her booked into the hospital. I watched Granny being carried down into the ambulance on a stretcher. Daddy was in there with her. I went running to follow, but my mum stopped me at the front door. She was telling me I wasn't allowed in the ambulance. "I have to go and see Granny!" I was shouting. "I have to give her a kiss and say goodbye!" I was telling her, but she wasn't budging. "She'll be back tomorrow and you can kiss her then." My mum said. But I told my mum she wouldn't be coming back and that I had to see her now. Tomorrow would be too late... She just kept telling me to go back in the house, but I wouldn't listen. "I have to say goodbye because she's going to die!" I screamed... My mum told me off for saying this and said it was a horrible thing to say. She told me to stop being silly and that I still wasn't allowed.

My dad must have heard all the drama from inside the ambulance. He poked his head out and told mum to let me come. I went running to my granny's side, then just stopped.

I stared down at her all wrapped in blankets and strapped onto the bed. I was in shock to see her like this, as I hadn't ever seen anyone in an ambulance before..."I love you, Granny" I said... Afraid to touch her and not sure if I should kiss her, in case I hurt her. She was in and out of consciousness, but seemed to come round at that moment. She stared up at me and smiled, giving a slight nod to say she understood and loved me too. I was touched by the effort she made. She was so weak and in so much pain, yet she found the strength to lift her arm and take my hand to give it a little squeeze. We just gazed at each other for a moment... "Goodbye, Granny," I said... Then my attention was taken by my mum stood at the ambulance doors.

"Okay now? You've said bye... come on!" she said... I kissed Granny on the cheek, then turned to jump out of the ambulance... That was the last time I saw my granny alive. She died the next day in hospital.

I got home from school the next day and was being looked after by babysitters. I was constantly asking what time everyone would be back and if they had called yet. I wasn't told anything. I was told to go and get ready for bed, but I wouldn't move off the sofa in the big bay window. I insisted that I wasn't moving until they were back and I knew Granny was all right. I was starting to feel very sleepy from 8pm onwards and was really fighting not to fall asleep. I just kept staring at the clock. That's how I know the exact time my eyes couldn't fight anymore and at 8:30pm I fell asleep. During that time I dreamt of Granny. I dreamt I was in another room watching her lay on her bed, when she suddenly just fell out and rolled onto the floor. She pulled herself up and began crawling towards me, every now and then reaching out her arm for me to help her. I was just frozen in my dream and couldn't move. I felt scared too. Then as she got close to me, she just dropped and stopped moving. I started trying to scream for Daddy, but no voice would come out of my mouth, just a whisper. Then with all the panic I awoke with a start! First of all still in shock from the dream I'd just had, then worried how long I had been asleep. I looked at the clock instantly. The time now was 8:40pm. I was angry at myself for falling asleep. So now made sure I was going to stay awake.

Finally I heard the cars - they were home. My mum walked in first. She stopped as she walked in the living room and stopped when she saw me. "Oh, you're still awake?" she said.

My reply was, "She's dead isn't she?"

Mum didn't answer my blatant question.

"Come to the dining room in a minute," she said. Then I watched my uncle from Belgium come in, my uncle who lived with us and my aunty from London, who had recently married. I couldn't believe how fast they had all got here (as we lived in Nottinghamshire.) I knew for sure then that something was wrong. Finally my daddy walked in. "Oh hello, my darling," he said to me, then carried on through to the dining room. I followed him through and was given the news. The strangest thing was though... when told, the biggest smile came to my face. I just couldn't stop it. Then the tears came... I couldn't stop sobbing for so long. That was one of the few times I remember my mum holding me for so long as I sobbed on her shoulder.

For years I hated myself for that instant smile in response to the dreadful news of my granny's death. Why would I smile? How awful of me! Only now do I understand that smile and no longer feel shame... I truly was happy for her and my spirit body knew so – she was finally out of pain, at peace and in a wonderful place. I knew she was safe now and would be happy. What actually made me cry was seeing the sadness in my daddy's face and watching him cry. My daddy told me that my granny died at exactly 8:37pm, which is the exact time that I was born (not the same date though). He found this fact rather special, as did I... I also realised that sleep overtook my battle just before that time. I was asleep at the time of my granny's death and awoke a couple of minutes after. I watched her give up the fight, right before my very eyes. I told Daddy about my dream at that same time and it's a story he still tells people now. Only for that short ten minutes did I fall asleep and in that time my granny passed.

Chapter 4

Crystal Ball

My mum and dad owned a residential care home for the mentally handicapped. I would spend a lot of time there. Two staff that worked at the home were called Carol and Shirley. I loved Carol and Shirley! They always treated me so well and would often babysit for me too. They made me feel special. They were both Spiritualists and I know for sure that Shirley saw spirit and practiced mediumship. I always remember a special look she would often give me and tell me "You're a very special little girl, you know that? You've got a gift and one day you will use it well." I didn't have a clue what she was talking about at the time, but it made me feel good anyway. Carol and Shirley would go to the spiritualist meetings once every week. I did not have a clue what went on there, but for some reason I was intrigued and would beg my parents to let me go with them. They seemed happy to take me, but I think my parents just didn't want to impose. Eventually, as ever, I got my own way. However when attending with the ladies, I really did not understand a word they were saying, or what was happening. So much so I don't remember anything of the meeting and didn't want to go again. While I was there a man stood at the front of the audience, where I was sat with Carol and Shirley. I now know he was the medium delivering messages from spirit. I didn't know this at the time as it might have helped! The one thing I remember is the medium coming to me. He pointed me out to all of the audience and said "Hello" to me. I remember feeling a bit shy and embarrassed. He then said that I was a very special little girl with a strong gift, then moved onto the next person. Carol and Shirley were very eager to tell my mum that the medium spoke to me. When I look back I think it's quite interesting that even at that young age of nine years old, I was so naturally interested in this activity, even though I didn't really understand it.

Every time anyone said I was special, when I was younger, I just thought they were being kind because of the colour of my skin and the fact that Daddy was black. I grew up in a small town, where out of the few hundred people that lived there, there was less than twenty people of colour. My darker skin tone was never made an issue by anyone. However, I liked being different anyway. It made me feel special. One evening Carol and Shirley came over to our house with a crystal ball. They had bought it for my mum to use. They were going to teach my mum how to use it to help her de-stress, relax and maybe see my granny. After Granny passed my mum seemed to have a few issues of letting go. She kept needing to know that Granny was alright and I think Shirley and Carol were trying to help her with this. I wasn't supposed to know anything about this, obviously... But I kept hiding and eavesdropping. Again I was overly intrigued. Drawn like a magnet and wanting to be involved. I wasn't allowed in the dining room for the time the three of them sat with the crystal ball, but I kept sneaking peeks through the kitchen window which looked into the dining room. At this point I didn't know they were trying to look for Granny in the ball. As I looked in, through the window I saw Granny in the room with them. It's hard to explain, as I didn't see her like I would see another person before me. She was in my mind's eye. I knew she was there, I knew where she stood and knew what she was wearing. I was confused myself at this and was unsure. As much as I was told I mustn't go in the dining room I just had to go in and ask. "Is Granny here?" They all looked at me funny and surprised.

"Why would you say that? Can you see her?" my mum asked.

Well I didn't know how to answer this. I couldn't see her. Not like I was seeing everyone else in the room. So I said "No."

They let me stay after this though. I listened and watched what they were doing. My mum was sat with the crystal ball. She gazed into it, her hands surrounding it. From the gist of the conversation I understood she was trying to see Granny. I'm not sure if she did, but I wanted a go! I started pestering and pestering to have a go myself. If they could see Granny in the crystal ball I wanted to see her too. Either I was very persuasive as a child, or I was just so annoying people would give me what I wanted to shut me up... But again they gave in.

They showed me to sit and just look into it the ball with my hands around the ball, but not actually touching it. "What now?" I asked.

"Just get to know it." Carol said to me. "You have to become familiar with it first."

Again I didn't understand much, so I just thought "Get to *know* it" So I did. I chatted away to it in my head. "Hello! How are you? My name is Soonita. I don't really know what to do with you but they're all looking for Granny inside you. If she's there can I see please?" I quickly began to see mist in the ball that parted like clouds. I'm not sure if it was my imagination, or what they call your inner eye. A long dark tunnel spiralled above me with a light at the top and a person peering down to me. I thought for some reason that this place must be heaven, therefore Granny would be there. I asked the person at the top of the tunnel if she knew my Granny and could fetch her for me, as I really wanted to see her. She nodded. I saw the lady drift and a ray of white moving lights, then I blinked. As I refocused on the ball the tunnel and the lady were gone. Instead, as the fog cleared in the ball, I saw my Granny. "I see Granny!" I shouted. Mum, Shirley and Carol came gathering around me. I'm not sure if they believed me.

"What does she look like? What is she wearing?"

I described what I saw. I saw her just as the first time when I laid eyes on her at the airport. Then her hair changed. It was now out of the plait and loose, coming round her shoulders. There was a glow around her and I got a real sense of calm and peace.

Shirley was getting quite uncomfortable. She was saying how I shouldn't have been allowed to use the crystal ball as I was too young. "Leave her a minute!" Carol said. "Out of all of us, she is the only one to see anything in that ball tonight. I knew she had it! I told you she was special!" Carol seemed genuinely rejoiced for me, but Shirley being ever so cautious as usual, wasn't best pleased. They looked at my mum as if to say "What do you think?" I guess as I'm her child. Mum just looked deep in thought and teary.

"Ask her if she's okay?" my mum said. She was referring to Granny of course. As my mum asked the question my Granny immediately smiled and nodded to me.

"She's smiling, Mummy," I said. "I think she's happy."

After that Mum seemed to pull herself together and told me that was enough now and that I shouldn't really have used it because I was so young. Carol went to pick up the ball to put it away. "Oh my God!" she blurted, with the ball in her hand. "Feel how hot the ball is!" Everyone had a feel and it was very really quite hot (not as to burn you though).

"Why is it hot?" I asked.

"From you!" Carol replied. I was confused as I hadn't even touched it the whole time. In fact my arms got tired holding my hands up near the ball so I just rested them on the table quite away from the ball, but I could still see. I said this to the ladies. "You were putting your energies into it to use it," Carol explained. "Your energies heated it up! You must have very strong energies."

Well I still didn't understand too much. I remember Carol banging on about me for the rest of the evening though and

Shirley's disapproval. My mum just told me that it was best that we didn't tell Daddy about this as it might upset him to hear us talk about Granny and that he doesn't agree with all this anyway. I did as I was told with this one. I was just so grateful I got to see Granny again.

After that incident I banged on and on how I wanted a crystal ball of my own. I would always pester Carol to bring her ball for me to use again. She did bring it once more and I was allowed to use it again. This time however I just chatted to it in my mind, as before with my hands resting on the table and gazing into it from above. I was more fascinated that the ball heated up so much last time and rather taken by the fact everyone seemed so impressed by this. So part of my conversation with the ball was asking it to get really hot again so I could impress everyone. Sure enough within a couple of minutes the ball heated up fast and I shouted Mum and Carol to come feel. Carol sat with me, obviously intrigued as to what I was capable of with this ball. She said to me "Right, I'm going to tell you my granddad's name and I want you to see if you can see him in the ball OK? Just really concentrate."

OK, I thought. So I carried on chatting to the ball in my head, very matter of factly. "OK, so Carol wants me to try and see her granddad inside you, ball, can you show me? I think it will make her very happy." Immediately the spiral long tunnel rose above me again, with the light at the top and a lady stood there peering down. I figured her granddad must be dead, as I was shown heaven once again. Or what I imagined to be heaven. "Oh hello again," I said to the lady. "You're the one who fetched my granny to me last time aren't you?"

I heard her reply in my mind, "Yes... Who would you like me to bring now?"

I thanked her very much for bringing my Granny and said how lovely of her it was. I spoke very respectfully to this lady as I knew she was really special. "I would be really grateful if you can bring Carol's granddad to me, please." I said his name and I saw her leave. Moments later a saw a man in the ball, from the shoulders up. Even though I couldn't see the rest of his body I knew what he was wearing. I described to Carol what I saw and she was thrilled.

"That's him!" she said with tears in her eyes. She gave me a big kiss and a hug and told me I was really very special. I suppose I felt like I was pleasing people and as a child it always feels good to please people. I didn't really understand exactly what I was doing and the fact I was communicating to spirit. It was almost like a game to me, that I was good at... I was never very good at that much.

Leading up to Christmas I kept saying that I wanted a crystal ball. I preached on about that being the most important present and the one thing I wanted the most. Mum kept saying "No" and that I was too young. Sure enough, however, on Christmas day I was delighted to unwrap a crystal ball. "Is it real?" I asked in surprise. Mum explained that it was, but I must never use it. She said it was just to sit in my bedroom and that would help me to feel happy and protect me. "Protect me from what?" I asked. She didn't answer my question again... She was good at that. She just replied that it was to be used purely as an ornament for my bedroom and nothing else. She said if she ever caught me using it for anything else that she would take it away from me. Well I didn't want to risk that did I? I nodded and smiled, knowing that I was going to have to be extra careful about not getting caught.

I think Mum must have spoken to Carol about whether she should get me the crystal ball. Knowing what I know now about certain crystal balls and their different properties, I can only think Carol suggested it to be a wise idea. If I was able to communicate with spirits, it would be important that I was protected from any evil spirit that may want to come near. I know now that evil spirits do exist. Thankfully I have never experienced this, but I trust in my sweet spirit guide, Mary, to keep me protected from any unpleasant entities coming close to me, or being able to communicate.

I did so want to use my ball as soon as possible. But I was scared to use it alone. I think it actually started to dawn on me that I was playing with the unknown and I just sensed that I did need to be careful. I waited for my chance. Babysitters! Whenever I needed babysitting, Mum would leave me at the care home with the staff on duty at that time. The staff didn't seem to mind. All the residents in the home were just like my family and I loved being there and having lots of people around all the time. Some of the residents had the mentality of a young child, so it was just like having friends to play with my own age, just bigger in size than me. This particular evening a lady called Sheila (change of name to hide true identity) was looking after me. I told her about my crystal ball and that I could see dead people inside it. I don't think she believed me at first, which made me more determined to prove myself.

"*Honestly,*" I said. "Just tell me the name of someone you know who has died and I will find him in my crystal ball!" She wasn't sure at first and would say that I shouldn't dabble in these kind of things, especially being so young. Eventually however, she gave me a name. I sat down with my ball. After five minutes Sheila stopped what she was doing and came to sit down next to me.

"Can you see anything then?"

I said yes, but wasn't sure if I had the right person. I described to her what I saw. I described his outfit, his hair, his blue eyes (even though I was not seeing him in colour), the fact he was very old, and the way he was stood with his head up proud and tilted slightly to the side. He was giving a little look as if to say "Cheeky..."

With a smile on his face. Sheila was amazed and began to cry. She said I was exactly right with his description and that how I described him was the last time she saw her grandfather "He used to tease us as we were leaving his house," she said. "We knew every time we visited, that he gave us a pound each as we left. Sometimes he would pretend like he had forgotten, then at the last minute give it to us. He was stood at the door waving to us as we drove away in the car, he would have that same look on his face."

She believed me now. I was excited that not only had I managed to see her grandfather in the ball, but that I had proved myself again. She was emotional at first, but happy. Then she became a little spooked out by it. "I'm not sure about this," she said. "I don't think you should tell your parents about this, they'll go mad at me."

"It's OK." I said. "I've done it before... I just see them, nothing happens."

Well I was happy. Not only had I finally got to use my crystal ball, but it was confirmed that my ball was real. Just like Carol's.

The next time Sheila babysat me, there was another lady with her too. I began asking again for a name, so I could look into the ball to see them and describe them to her. Her friend wasn't sure whether to believe what she was hearing, from our last experience. I think it was because of this that Sheila gave in and finally said I could do it again. Her friend gave a name this time, as it was her that needed the proof. When I saw the man in my ball this time, it confused me a bit. The more I made out his face I felt some discomfort in what I was seeing. His face was big, taking up most of the ball. It was flat as if it had been rolled out with a rolling pin. I could make out the colour of his hair, the length and that he wore a loop earring in his ear and that he was young, like an older teenager. There were lots of scars going across his face like lightning bolts. But the scars were red, as if they were still bleeding. I started to explain what I saw and kept highlighting that it just didn't seem right, as if his face had been squashed. What she told me next sent a shiver down my spine and was enough to make me not play with my ball again for quite some time.

The man I saw had had a motorbike accident. The lady who had given me the name had witnessed his horrific death and watched him come flying off his motorbike and straight under a moving lorry. The wheel of the lorry had gone right over his face, flattening it and he died instantly. I began to realise something. What I saw in the ball was the person as *they* had seen them last. It scared me that I had seen the image of this scene, knowing that it was real and not just some horrible movie. The realisation kicked in of what I was actually doing and that it wasn't a game.

It was over a year later that I built up the courage to have another go. This time my aunty was babysitting. For some reason I felt like talking about things. It still played on my mind and disturbed me, but I couldn't talk to anyone about it. As I opened up to her and told her everything, I could see a slight unbelieving look in her face. This was frustrating me to the point where I felt I needed to prove myself again. Just to prove I wasn't lying. I begged for her to give me a name of someone she knew who had passed. She thought, but said she didn't know anyone who had. Finally she mentioned one person, but said she didn't really want to say as, if it was true what I said before, she didn't want me getting scared again. I insisted she told me the name. Eventually she did, so I looked into the ball. I started by chatting to the ball and apologising for not talking to it for so long (in my mind of course), then I did the usual rigmarole. Sure enough a face appeared to me. The image didn't scare me straight away. The head was tilted and looking down, hair coming into his face and his tongue hanging out.

Remember, I only ever asked for the person's name. I didn't know their age or anything else about them. This was a young man. Eyes bulging out and just glaring. "Oh my God!" My aunty exclaimed, shocked... Not only had I described him accurately, but the way I saw him disturbed her too. "Why is his tongue out though?" I asked. "How did he die? Is that how he looked the last time you saw him?" She wouldn't tell me at first and she seemed very anxious.

"Promise you are not going to tell your mum and dad about this," she said. "He hung himself. He was off his head and had taken lots of drugs. He was my best friend's boyfriend and he'd been calling her all night. We went to find him later and when we finally did, we found him hanging in a barn... That was exactly how I saw him last, just as you'd described." Again I was alarmed at the reality of what I had just seen. A real man hanging, dead. After that time it was nearly twenty years later, until I used the crystal ball again.

I kept the ball up on a shelf in my bedroom. There were times when I felt as if the ball was calling to me. As if someone was trying to get through to communicate to me. It spooked me out at times, so I would hide the ball behind a book or something. I could never get rid of it though, or smash it, or throw it away. Someone told me that once you have a ball it always belongs to you and if you ever smashed it or threw it away it was really bad luck. I can't remember who told me that, but the words stuck. One time I hadn't been in my room for some time. There was no explanation for what I saw when I went into my room, as I was alone in the house. The crystal ball was all condensed and misty. Just like a car window when lots of people are sat in it with no windows open. How? I thought. I had seen it like that before, but only when I had been using it for a long time. A drip of condensation even slid down the side of it. I picked it up to dry it thinking it was very odd. When I did, I realised it was so hot! Like someone had been using it. "It heats up when it's gathered energy" I remembered Carol's words. Well, it wasn't my energy and there was no one else around. I can also assure you that the ball was not sat in sunlight as the shelves I kept it were set back and in the shade. It was also a cold winter's day. I put it back quickly and instinctively said a prayer asking God to protect me and keep me safe. I'm sure if there was anyone in spirit trying to get through to me, that they would not be bad. I was just scared because I didn't understand... but I know a spirit did try to get through to me, through that ball.

Chapter 5

Precognitions and Dreams to Fall True

From being very young I remember experiencing many moments as what I would refer to as Deja vu, only it wasn't Deja vu. These moments would be full clear memories of dreams I had. Momentary dreams of waking in another bedroom and taking notice how all the furniture was set out. At the time making no sense to me and not even knowing why the dream had stuck in my head. Then a year later I awake in my new bedroom which my parents kitted out and placed all the furniture, to realise that the dream I had was of this very room. I had known it, before I lived it.

I had a great Aunty Marion who passed away when I was very young at around four to five years old. I remember she had very strawberry blonde, light gingery hair and was very attractive. We did not see her often, then one night out of the blue I dreamt of her saying goodbye to me. A couple of days later she passed away. The same thing happened with my Great Grandma Tordoff from my mother's side. About a month before she passed away I dreamt she came to me in my bedroom, sat at the end of my bed and told me that she was going away and wouldn't be coming back, however I would see her again, but not for a very long time. She told me that she loved me and always thought a lot of me. As she stood to walk out my bedroom it suddenly hit me that she meant she was going die. A heavy sadness weighed on me, followed by gratitude for her coming to say goodbye. I was fourteen years old at the time and my mother had left into a house of her own. My mum and dad split up when I was fourteen years old. I told my dad about the dream the very next morning and he told me not to tell my mum as it would upset her. I asked him if he thought the dream meant she was going to die soon. He said she would go anytime now since she was already one hundred years old. Her birthday was in four weeks' time to me having this dream. I told my dad that morning that she wouldn't make it to her one hundred and first birthday. She died two days before her birthday. God bless her.

I was about ten years old, when we were driving down some roads and lanes we had never been on before. It was late at night after a family party and we were following my Uncle's car in front to guide us back to his house where we would stay for the night. The roads were pretty clear, as it was so late. All the way I kept saying to my mum, "We've been here before, I recognise these roads, and we've been here!" My mum was getting rather annoyed with me as she was trying to concentrate on the roads and following my Uncle's car. "I can assure you, Soonita, we have not been here before, I haven't got the faintest idea where we are, which is why I can't lose sight of Uncle's car! Now let me concentrate!" My youngest brother was only one year old at the time.

I just knew I had seen these roads before, so I began describing what would be coming up ahead next, as we weaved round the roads. "Just past these houses we go through some road with big tree's either side, then some more houses." Sure enough everything I was describing before it came, turned out to be right. "Just round the corner here there will be some shops on the right!" My aunty was in the back of the car with me and was getting a little spooked out by this.

"Are you sure you haven't been here before?" she asked my mum again.

"Absolutely sure!" replied my mum with a snap!

This went on for some time, then ... BANG! It hit me! I realised why I knew these roads! I had dreamt this journey before! I excitedly told everyone in the car, satisfied that it was explained as to why I knew these roads. Then I remembered the last part of the dream. In my dream we had approached some traffic lights at a crossroads. Mum was driving and following a car. As the lights began to change the first car went through and my mum followed, just in time before the lights turned red... only it wasn't in time, as a small red car approaching from the right crossed us at such a speed and crashed straight into us! Spinning our car off the road! The other car had gone through a red lights.

As the memory of this dream came back to me I began telling it as fast as I could and pleading with my mum that she must stop at the next lot of lights, no matter what! She was not happy about this! Not only was I distracting her, but the idea of her losing the car in front was a terrible thought, as she didn't want to end up lost, with three kids in the car, late at night. My aunty looked at me and just put her seat belt on. She said "Well I'm not chancing it! You're scaring me now!" My mum tried to reassure me that there couldn't even be lights ahead with a big cross roads that I'd described as it was just lanes with trees. What I was describing sounded more like a built up area. Sure enough, as we came round another corner the whole scenery changed and we were approaching the crossroads with lights that I had described. There were no other cars in sight apart from my Uncle's in front. I was nearly in tears shouting at my mum to stop at the lights, but she kept on going... Right up until the last second where she slammed her breaks on, out of anger, I think just to shut me up. At that moment as she turned to tell me off for causing such a scene while she was driving, the small red car passed at such a speed! We wouldn't have stood a chance. Everyone just went silent in the car, in shock, as the realisation of what could have just been, set in... Well at least I was out of trouble... and we were all still alive!

We had not long moved to Essex with my Ddd in 2001, when I had this most frightening dream! I dreamt that a plane was flying low shooting bullets from its wings attacking everyone and everything in sight. In my dream my youngest brother was a toddler again and I was trying desperately to protect him. Bullets were flying around all over and I was trying to keep us away from the windows. Everything went silent for a moment so I looked out of the bedroom window and as I looked to my right, down the road I saw a massive passenger aeroplane coming in so low , I knew it was about to tear through the houses either side of the street. It did exactly that, all the way to end of our street and swooping up and away. Surviving this I momentarily felt relieved, until I looked again and saw another plane coming in low to do the same thing, from the other direction. As I saw it coming my final thoughts were "A World War has started!" I watched it tear through the first few houses either side of the street, before running to get my brother and thankfully waking up! A month later the Twin Towers of New York were terrorised, killing thousands. Shortly following the announcement that a War was beginning... To which is still ongoing, sadly.

In my dream, the two sides of the road with houses were symbolic of the Twin Towers. The planes coming in low to tear through them depicted the planes going into the Towers. In my dream there were two planes, as there were in the destruction of the two towers... There were also two planes that came separately and from two different directions. In a flash it all made sense. I remember feeling utterly shocked and completely devastated over what happened.

The timing was incredible. Just as I walked through the front door to my home, my dad was sat with the news on. I walked in to the first plane literally just hitting the first tower. I couldn't believe what I was seeing and feeling so desperately worried for the people trapped inside. Not long after I watched the second plane hit the other tower, fires blazing and people jumping from the building to their deaths. I couldn't take my eyes away, knowing that one of the towers was about to collapse and just praying so hard in my thoughts, drowned with tears for the people to be helped. I watched as the towers came tumbling down. Tears flowing and barely being able to breath at the sight... and the knowing that at that moment, so many lives were being tragically stolen from the Earth. Thousands of families being ripped apart in such devastating circumstances. I cried so much over this and still do now when thinking of it, or hearing stories linked to it.

One night, not long after this, I dreamt I was riding on a tube train in the back carriage, looking out the back window at the dark tunnel. I don't think this would be possible of the normal London Tubes as there are driver carriages either end of the trains. Suddenly I saw a fire ball shoot down the tunnel towards the train I was in. There were big explosions, fire and dust everywhere. I suddenly had a bird's eye view of all the tunnels on the underground, to see that three trains had explosions on them. The dust began to settle on the train I was in and I could see all the injuries of people and people laid dead, or literally in pieces. There was a whole arm with no body attached right next to me. Suddenly I became aware of a fourth train which came crashing through the wall of one of the tunnels and hitting the train I was in, so there was a second impact. When awaking from this dream I just laid in bed. In my thoughts saying "Please God, no, don't let this be true."

My youngest brother (who at the time was about fourteen years old) was staying over in Essex with us at the time and was due to get the train back up north, from Kings Cross that morning. I'd had this dream about a month previous to this day... I was due to work at a nearby nursery I was helping out at, so would not have been able to assist my brother back that day. My partner Chris said he would take the day off work to take him for me. I couldn't put my finger on it at the time! I just knew I wasn't happy about this. I kept trying to persuade my brother to wait until the weekend to go back, that way Chris and I could go to London together and spend the day. Two birds with one stone, as they say. But my brother wouldn't budge – his mind was made as he had a party or something to get back for... kids! My brother had booked his ticket to leave Kings Cross for about 10am that morning, so my brother and Chris would have had to leave home early to make it there in good time.

I remember falling out with Chris the night before trying hard to talk him out of taking him. I was angry with my brother for not changing his mind... Yet I was still telling Chris to have the day off work? Only he worked in London so he would have had to travel on the tubes as usual if going to work... I was getting annoyed and confused with myself as I couldn't explain these feelings I was having... Everyone else around me was also getting angry with me as I seemed to be kicking off about nothing. That night, before bed, I sat feeling defeated and crying. I said a little prayer to god, which may have sounded for selfish reasons at the time... but just begging God to not let them go tomorrow. "Please, God, I don't want them travelling tomorrow, it would be best to wait for the weekend, let them see that would be best, God, please!"

The next morning as I left the house early to go to work, I knew Chris would be getting up soon to take my brother to

London. As I was still annoyed with him from the night before I didn't even wake him to say goodbye. The next thing, I was at work looking after the babies in the small room of the nursery. The manager came rushing down to say that there had been explosions on the London Undergrounds and that we can make calls to check if loved ones are all right, if they travel by tube. Of course I did straight away! Turns out both Chris and my brother had slept long after their alarms going off, so hadn't even left the house at the time of the explosions in London. My prayers had truly been answered and I finally understood why I had so not wanted for them to travel that day... thank you, God xx

It wasn't until the tragic incidents of the tube bombings that I gave thought to the dream I'd had. As more details of the tragedy unfolded, my dream became clearer. Due to the explosion of one train near Aldergate Station, another train on the other side of the tunnel derailed, crashing through the wall of the tunnel... Just like in my dream. For a while after that, travelling on the tubes for me was difficult... Especially when I went through stations near where the explosions took place. I would get flashes of my dream coming into my head, I would hear screams of people running to get out to safety and feel the panic in my chest and stomach... I was experiencing visions of what had happened every time I went near these places and it would be difficult to pick myself back up to feel in a good mood again for whatever we were out and about doing. Because of my dream and experiencing that moment, I truly felt connected to what had happened and the people that had gone through it... being on those very trains at the time, the fear and panic rushing through them... I truly felt for each of them. I felt for those that witnessed terrible scenes that will never leave them, for those racing to get back up to higher ground in fear of more explosions, for families not being able to get in touch with loved ones to make sure they were all right... and so on and so on...

I know now, that the visions and feelings I would pick up on when near these stations was due to residual energies. This is memory that the surrounding physical walls, floors or objects can hold within them, for centuries after, depending on the incident and impact of it at the time... These energies can be left lingering within the atmosphere of that vicinity alone, so someone can just walk through it and sense and feel tragedy or upset. More of us than we realise are sensitive to these left over energies. How many times have you been out and about and suddenly you just feel, sad, low, lack of energy or even suddenly angry and in a bad mood and you don't even know what triggered it! This could be knock on effects of walking through, or coming into contact with lower energies around you.

Some people have the ability to hold onto objects, for example a piece of jewellery and read from it... they can give you information about the person that piece of jewellery belongs to and where it has been, or what experiences it has absorbed. They do this by connecting with the residual energies that object, or piece of jewellery holds. This is called Psychometry.

For some reason immediately after giving birth to my beautiful girl, my psychic abilities and pre cognitive dreams heightened immensely. At this time I still was not aware of the abilities I held within me. I would have a random dream in the night of something bizarre or a particular event taking place. In the morning I would get up with my new born baby, where something would happen within the first hour to bring that dream to light. Sometimes my daddy, or partner might ring with some particular news. Most of the time though it would be that first instant I turned on the telly. Within five minutes my dream would come to light. It got to the point where it became a bit of a joke with myself. I would turn on the TV, smiling and knowing what would be being talked about on the news, GMTV, or This Morning. For whatever reasons, after about a year of giving birth, these dreams began to lessen. However, did not stop completely.

Chapter 6

The Dark Days of My Teens

From the age of ten I battled a lot with my weight. Mum and Dad worked long hours and I would have all different people looking after me, or one of them would be around but be busy. I had no one to monitor what I ate and when... It was only really my dad that made sure we ate good food daily and he would cook every day making sure we ate fresh food... This would be at least for one meal a day. The rest of the day would be snacking on whatever was available. By the age of thirteen to fourteen I started to starve myself quite a lot, or went through phases of binge eating, then feeling bad for it and making myself sick. I was not ever really directed on the right foods to eat in order to be slim and healthy. Fortunately by the age of sixteen years old I educated myself a little better on the topic and would do exercise and yoga and choose to eat certain things that were slightly healthier for me.

Starting secondary school there was a shift of innocence. Up until this point I was pretty sheltered from anything sexual in nature. My parents were not even affectionate to each other, so to see people even kiss, I felt embarrassed. From my first year in secondary school I was being exposed to kids my own age making out in the wash rooms like it was normal! It was always the real pretty girls of my year and the year above, with different boys all the time. Thinking back... compared to a lot of girls in my year at that time, I was still like a little girl... Innocent.

I think that's part of why a lot of people began to take to me... I was innocent AND gullible... and to top it off... fearless... Other kids could ask me to do something and I would just do it. I'd hear friends talking and phrases like "blow job" would come up. "What's a blow job?" I would innocently ask... everyone would crack up, but even they would be too embarrassed to say. "Go and ask the teacher," they would say... so I did. No one would tell me. I asked about three teachers and two dinner ladies and my poor parents when I got home. It's wasn't until about three days later a friend actually told me. Then I still didn't believe her! So I asked one more teacher if this was true, who bravely turned to me and said, "Yes, Soonita..." Bless 'em!

I made best of friends with a girl called Lacey (change of name) who was pretty much top dog of our year. No one messed with her and Gina, my other good friend. Not even the boys, or else they would get a good pasting too! I felt safe with these girls, though they would also have a few jokes on me at times... being as gullible as I was... but when I was alone with Lacey, she really was kind and gentle to me. I had gone from being a girl at primary school who always tried her hardest and never got into trouble to quite a troublesome teenager at secondary school. I got to a point where I just gave up trying to please people, as it seems no matter how hard I tried, I couldn't. Every year at primary school my school report would be the same. "Soonita could have done better." I tried so bloody hard! I just wasn't naturally academically gifted! I was one of those kids that always had to try that bit harder to do well. Starting secondary school was my last chance. I did try hard with my school work the first year and making sure all my homework was in on time, only to receive the same jargon from my end of year report. "Soonita could have done better." That was it... that was my breaking point and that is where I turned to the world and said, "Fuck it!"

I had a lot of stuff going on at home as well. I had my mum who was riddled with anger living under the same roof as the woman my dad was having an affair with, who was jealous of me and my dad's relationship... plus my mum and Dad were going through hard times losing their businesses. I have the most fantastic father! But he was a shit husband... that's for sure. Boy! Did I have some stories to tell at school! Kids would flock around me to listen to my bizarre home life! Weirdly, I just took all of this on the chin. I felt for my parents but it was hard for me to really understand the real emotions of the situations and the hurt. Partly because of my age and partly because I was always stuck in the middle of it getting shouted at all the time.

My dad's girlfriend would often make up lies about me or exaggerated things to make me sound worse, so my dad would tell me off. That would really get to me. I hated my dad being annoyed with me, especially when I was innocent! He was my world and my everything. He still is, alongside my daughter and my husband. But back then... He was my all! The more he got angry with me, the more I felt angry towards him for not understanding, or believing me.

So! All of this before I was officially a teen... and that wasn't all to come before the age of thirteen. The massive shift in my life and of more to come was when I went away with my mum and her family for a camping holiday to Scarborough. We went away for a week. I was with my cousin, Shelly, who was three years older than me. We shared a tent. I always envied my cousin. She was so beautiful with her itty bitty waist line, blonde hair and pretty face. Next to her I felt short, fat and ugly. She had this sense of air about her. A confidence in knowing that she was beautiful and exactly what to do when approached by boys. She was extremely sexual and very active in that department and it's as if men just sensed it about her.

Everywhere we walked heads would turn to look at her in admiration. With plenty of make-up, heels and skimpy clothing, I managed to get into the club where you had to be over fifteen years to get in. It was just like a night club with the odd acts on stage etc... Your usual cheesy British holiday sight. We just happened to be sat near a table full of other kids about my cousin's age and a bit older, who all started coming over to talk. A girl called Rachel came over first to tell my cousin that her mate fancied her. The boys obviously used these girls for reeling in other girls... and it worked! I was a bit shy with the boys so stuck to talking to Rachel, whilst my cousin Shelly was in full flow with the boys! They had snuck in bottles of vodka which they were putting in our drinks of lemonade and coke... I had never touched Vodka! The most I'd had up until now was odd sips of my dad's beer!

Rachel and her gang were from a care home for kids in Sunderland. They were on a two week trip, the same week as us. They had been there a week already to when we arrived, so had already made other friends too. They had made friends with some boys in a tent, some boys on holiday with their Dad staying in a chalet and now us! We got introduced to everyone! As the club drew close to closing time the gang weren't ready to stop yet! We said how we had to get back to our tent as our parents would be expecting us, then Shelly said we could still meet them out later in the night as we could sneak out. I was mortified! And really didn't want to do this. Not only out of fear of getting caught, but I was actually scared by the thought of been out in the night so late and alone, without an adult... remember, up to this point I was still pretty innocent. My mum and dad barely let me go to the shop down the road on my own in broad day light! Never mind when it was dark!

When that moment came nothing was going to stop Shelly. "Fine I'll go on my own then!" She called me a few names as well for being a chicken. Despite her being a bit mean to me, I was worried for her to go out alone. So in the end I went along. We started out helping the kids from the care home climb out the windows of their caravan, then we were led the way to the chalet where the three boys were staying with their dad. Their dad was a very relaxed character who basically let the boys do what they wanted. None of them were over sixteen, but there they were, alcohol flowing! There were loads of us in that chalet! A little party going on. I felt so uncomfortable at first, but began to relax a little after a couple of cans of lager. Then everyone got bored and decided we would go out exploring.

This bit was pretty exciting. Security would drive around through the night and if you got picked up, you would be escorted back to where you were staying. I did not want this! So every now and then you would see the lights of the van coming and the torch shining and we would all scurry to hide. To say I never really drank, I'd had a lot this night and where did everyone decide to go? The edge of a cliff! We were so high up, you couldn't see anything at the bottom except darkness. However you could hear the sea crashing around. A few of the gang decided there must be a beach down below, so if we all climbed down we could spend some time messing about on the beach, in the pitch black... as you do... I tried to persuade Shelly for us to go now, but she was having none of it!! "Come on you woos!" So down the cliff we followed... We didn't even get half way down till everyone decided it was too dangerous and it just sounded like sea at the bottom. There was no path on this cliff going down. We were literally climbing, out of our heads on alcohol! How any of us are still alive I don't know!

On our way walking to the cliff a boy a couple of years older than me clung onto me. He was being sweet enough, but I certainly didn't fancy him. I thought he was being friendly and since my cousin pretty much abandoned me with her new friends, I appreciated the company. He was really sweet, giving me his jacket, holding my hand and helping down the cliff side etc... I did think it really weird that he started telling my how he only had one ball sack though! I just kept thinking to myself "Why would he be telling me this?" He was telling me a sob story of when he was little and had a cyst on his testicle and had to have the whole thing removed. Sad, I'm sure. Still didn't understand why he would share this information with me though... Gosh I was so naive! It all made sense later when we were sat on the cliff side, having a rest before making our way back up.

There at the age of twelve, I had my first proper kiss... It was fucking horrible! The boy practically swallowed my face! If this was what it was all about I did not see the pleasure! I was far too kind and polite to tell him this though. So he did it again and again and again... blurrrr! My cousin was very proud of me of course. I was becoming more like her, which she thought was great. Later it all came to light why he was telling me about his one ball, when he took my hand to put it down his trousers! I was so embarrassed! I'd only just had my first kiss that night, then this! I had the quickest feel, then pulled my hand away quick! I didn't know what to do with that! Mortified! To the extreme!

Later he started to feel really ill from all the alcohol so went back to his. Some other boys who were part of our big gang offered to walk me and Shelly back to our tent. Yes, how very kind... before they let us go we got a few more kisses. As much as I felt uncomfortable with it, I didn't know how to tell them "No". I felt I had no choice but to go along with it as my cousin would tell me off otherwise. So I got two more snogs before our evening was over from two more different boys. They weren't as bad as the first though... at least!

We crept back into our tent about 6am. We talked for about ten minutes. "So how was your first kiss? I can't believe you, Soonita, you're like a new girl! Well done!" Hmmm, still wasn't sure how I felt about the whole thing. Next thing I knew our mum's were screaming at us to get up for breakfast. It was 8:30am and they didn't want us sleeping the whole day away missing out on all the fun now did they? Hangover central! And in serious need of sleep!

The family went out to spend the day in Scarborough. Shelley and I went back to bed for a bit, then went off out to get into more trouble with the gang. Every night that week we were sneaking out in the middle of the night. With different boys getting up to more mischief... my cousin ended up having sex with three different boys throughout the week. I snogged about seven, but was fast starting to look forward to coming home. We were drinking through the days and in the night. This was a whole new way of life for me.

On our second night there we had to wait around a little while for the over fifteen's club to open. We waited in the family bar. There sat two incredibly good looking super fly boys... I have to admit I was quite taken by their bad boy looks and baggy jeans. So much so that I told my cousin. She said "Which one do you like?" I pointed out the shorter one of the two. She was happy as she found the taller one more attractive. "Leave it to me," she said with a wink... I begged her not to do anything as I felt really embarrassed! I never really admitted to anyone if I fancied someone. I was always quite shy in that department.

Before I knew it the boys had come over and were sat at our table. We just talked a little while, then some of our gang came in looking for us, so we went off with them. I found out that the boy I liked was seventeen years old and called Jamie. Throughout the week we would see them every now and then and just say "Hello." I remember my cousin telling me off for being honest to the boys about my age. "They'll never want to know you now they know your age!" Weirdly I felt glad about that. I was bowled over by his looks, but I still didn't want anything more than to just look. All the kisses before that were very much a case of me being too shy to speak up and say, "No."

On our final night, Shelly and I had already decided we would not be sneaking out that night. We knew our family would have us up early and helping to pack everything up, as we had to be off the sight by 10:30am. We were having a great time in the club with all our gang. Celebrating our final night together and all getting a bit emotional. We'd actually made some really good friends. Rachel was my favourite and we stayed friends for a long time after. Though they were good friends, they weren't necessarily the best influence on me. These kids all came from very troubled backgrounds, most were from the children's home and some with a Dad who was not the most responsible of parents. My cousin came from a background of sexual abuse and torment, herself... All these kids were on the highroad of self-destruction, anger and had nothing to lose... What else in life could hurt them... they were fearless and didn't care for consequences... little did I know I would soon be joining them on that journey.

To my surprise Jamie came over and started talking to me. He was telling me how much he liked me and had been watching me throughout the week, but was too shy to come over and talk half the time as I was always with a lot of people. The last dance came on and he asked me to dance. It was nice and we kissed. Then him and his mate who Shelly liked, offered to walk us back to our tent. They tried to persuade us to come back out in the night, but we knew better. We were already at deaths door with all the lack of sleep, excitement and heavy drinking over the week. The thought alone of the hectic day to follow was killing us! I have to admit I was truly flattered by the interest this incredibly good looking guy was showing me.

It was pretty late again and everyone was tucked up in their tents ready for the big day... Most people were leaving that same day off the site. The boys walked over to where the wash rooms and toilets were to say their good byes to us. I couldn't let them walk us to our tent as my mum would have gone mad. Jamie was asking for my number, but I couldn't give it to him. I would be so scared of him ringing the house. My dad would have flipped if a boy rang asking for me! I'm so glad now that I didn't give him my number, as he quickly turned at his first opportunity at getting me alone. Shelly went off into the toilets with her fella, to which Jamie came onto me full force. So many thoughts were rushing through my head.

Up until now I hadn't had the courage to tell any of the boys to stop or say "No" to them kissing me. I wanted Jamie to stop but started to question in my head... "I should be happy about this, why don't I want him to kiss me now?" I knew this was about to get a lot heavier than I had yet experienced as his hands started to go under my clothes. I wasn't ready for this... I didn't really know what "this" was at that very moment, but I just wasn't ready. I started to tell him to stop and push him away, but he just got heavier and more forceful. As I was getting louder he dragged me into the washrooms, slammed me against the sinks and put his hands in my trousers. The more I struggled the more he was hurting, but then if I didn't struggle he got further and would still hurt me.

He was laughing as he put his fingers in me, telling me how tight I was and I just needed to relax. I struggled so much, begging him to get off that when he pulled his hand out from my trousers there was blood. "You see! Now look what you've done, you just need to relax! Don't worry about the blood, it's normal for your first time." I was horrified as it suddenly hit me what he was about to do. This is it... This was how I was about to lose my virginity. I remembered what my cousin had said that he wouldn't want to know me if he knew how old I really was. I thought maybe he's forgotten so I reminded him I was only twelve years old! This just seemed to turn him on more and seem more determined... He also got some pleasure out the fact that this would be my first time. It hurt so much as he finally managed to get his thing into me. For a moment before it was fully in I was crying out in so much pain, he put his hand over my mouth to shut me up. I couldn't even breathe when he did this. Once he was in, he didn't take long... thank goodness... The fight was over. I think I went into complete shock. I remember just occasionally getting my breath amidst the pain to tell him to stop, but he ignored me... I think he was getting a thrill out of the whole situation.

As I was getting my trousers on after my cousin came in looking for us, with her fella. "Ah there you are, you two lovebirds been having fun?" The boys left us, but not after one last kiss. My head was spinning. I couldn't get my head round what had just happened or even understand it. I got my cousin to come to the toilet with me before heading back to our tent. "So did you actually have sex?" She asked me excitedly. I thought for a moment...

"Yeah I think so." I was trembling and still in shock... "What do you mean you think so? Did he put his thing in you?"

"Yes" I replied not even wanting to talk about it to her, feeling so misunderstood.

She hugged me excitedly and congratulating me. I smiled at her nervously thinking "Why are you happy? Why is this good?" I felt so confused. I told her it was really painful to wee and it was stinging, then I was horrified at all the pure red blood on the tissue when I wiped myself. She reassured me this was all normal after your first time and that the first time was always painful. "At least you've got the first out the way now!" She said smiling. I fell to sleep that night, confused, feeling sick, sharp pains in my stomach and throbbing down below. My body was a mess. I had bruises and grazes all over my body. My cousin thought this was hilarious and a true sign of a good night out... I didn't think so.

Chapter 7

More to Follow

On my return home I was really ill for about a week. This was most likely due to the lack of sleep, huge amounts of alcohol and being out in the cold a lot. My head was a mess. I kept thinking about everything over and over. Everything... From that point on my life had changed... I had changed. Bathing was so painful for over a week after the incident also. Sitting down in certain positions, or hard seating. I just hid laid on my bed for about a week.

After I was back for three days my friend, Lacey, rang me. "Why haven't you rung me? How was your holiday?" I started telling her about my new friends we met and some of the adventures we got up to, then about some of the boys I kissed. I never liked other people to see or hear me down. No matter what, I always tried to put a brave face on for others. Maybe it was my way of not admitting to myself and others how I really felt, like that would make me weak somehow. She couldn't believe what she was hearing! "Soonita! You're so naughty!" She laughed. "And?" She asked for more details...

"And what?" I replied.

"And... What else? You kissed all those guys... Is that all you did?" She asked giggling. I reluctantly told her about Jamie. As I told her that we had actually had sex I choked and tears streamed down my face. "Ohhhh my Goshhh!" She screamed! "That's great! What's the matter with you?"

"I don't know." I said through my tears "I just can't believe it I suppose."

"Well that's great!! Now you've got the first out the way you will be fine! What was it like?"

"It hurt." I replied. "It really hurt."

"Well that's normal, it always hurts the first time."

"Mmm... I'm still hurting from it." I admitted.

"Did he use something?"

"What?" I asked naively... No one ever talked to me about sex. No grown up's. Not at the age of twelve! The only sex education we'd had at school before that was the basic what goes where and how babies were made.

"Did he use a condom?" she asked impatiently, wanting all the details.

"Oh! No... I don't think so. I didn't see anything."

"What do you mean you didn't see anything? Did he stop to put one on? Surely you would have noticed?" Well in that case I knew he hadn't... I'm sure amongst all the struggling he did not put on a condom.

What strikes me is that I told my friend I hadn't wanted to do it and that I told him to stop several times. She just laughed. It all sounded so normal to her. She said not to worry about it now as I probably would never see him again and to just watch out that I'm not pregnant! The thought hadn't even crossed my mind at the time! Strangely I didn't have a period for about six months after that. Looking back with a wiser head, this was probably down to stress and shock of what had happened. I definitely wasn't pregnant though. I was so under educated in that department that the thought of possibly catching any diseases didn't even cross my mind. I was very lucky.

My friend kept pushing me after that, that now I was sexually active I really should go on the pill. Strangely without my even suggesting anything, my doctor said that going on the pill might actually help me menstrually. Mum was taking me backwards and forwards to the doctors as I was getting such bad pains in my stomach... Like bad period pains, but not bleeding. The doctor put me on the pill to help to regulate my periods and hopefully reduce the pain. It worked. I also felt relieved that if anything like that happened again, I knew I wouldn't get pregnant.

So by the age of thirteen I was on the pill. Just as well for what was to follow... I had begged my friend, Lacey, not to tell anyone about what I'd told her. But by the time we were back at school everyone seemed to know! The only way I could deal with this was to smile and make out everything was OK. So what I'd had sex? Lacey had got to see a new side to me. One she found very exciting. Well after hearing what I'd got up to on holiday I was up for all kinds of fun! Wasn't I?

We began sneaking out to the pubs and bars a lot. She knew people who her older brother hung out with and would occasionally get a bit of speed (amphetamines) off them. I was up for anything now... I knew that other times of boys coming onto me were going to happen and I just thought... Well what can I do about it? To to get wasted was a good start. I was getting more and more popular at school, people flocking round to hear my crazy stories of mischief. I would be out with massive groups of boys and girls in the streets and parks, with as much booze as my baggy tops and coats could carry.

My mum and dad were beside themselves. They'd lost complete control of me. They were always going mad at me. "You've been drinking again... What time do you call this?" Friends would call round for me and they would say I'm not allowed out, so I'd go anyway... then later they would be searching the streets and friends' houses for me... It was embarrassing! But back then I didn't see what I was doing to them. They had so much other stuff going on. By now they had lost their business and their marriage was really at breaking point. Without realising it at the time, I was making myself even more vulnerable. Strangely, despite the rough lot I was knocking about with... and I mean mainly the boys... The threats didn't come from them. We would go to parties and kiss and what not, but they were never threatening... It was the adults I had to be more weary of.

My dad had bought his dream home and just about managed to get all the building work done before losing his business to pay for it. This house was right next door to the house we lived in and where he had run his business. So we moved in! In an attempt to hold onto the old house he began renting the rooms out for money. He would make good friends with some of the tenants and go out drinking with them. One particular guy got quite friendly with him and started trying to befriend me. His name was Andy. I felt very on guard with him from the start. He was in his mid-thirties... I was thirteen. By now I had developed quite a mouth on me and had learnt to be quick to speak up on what I thought of people.

He started out always staring at me. Then I bumped into him in a bar a couple of times where he'd offer to buy me drinks. I would refuse him a lot, but Lacey would have a go at me for turning down free drinks! He would tell me things like... He was my dad's friend and wanted to look out for me. He would say that he had to keep an eye on me to make sure I was safe. He would do my head in! Some thirty-odd year old guy trying to cramp my style! I felt like I was out under my father's watch. However, being my dad's friends, at this point I did not want to be rude to him... That is until I started getting into trouble with my parents where he had grassed on me! Telling them details of where I'd been out and what I'd been up to. I went mental at him!

I would blatantly be rude to him in my dad's face. He seemed like he'd tried to befriend me before that. I just couldn't work him out. Then it all started getting far worse... He started saying things to my dad that he was really worried about me and what I was up to. He was telling my dad lies that he feared I was getting myself heavily involved in drugs and hanging out with some dangerous people... At this point... None of it was true! He even started telling my dad that he had seen me out in the bars when I'd been innocently staying over at a friend's house! My dad was going livid with me! Every day was a battle with my mum and dad and I was always being frowned upon. I had no one but my friends for comfort, so I would spend more and more time out with them... At their houses, knocking about the streets or occasionally at a bar.

There was a pay phone in the house next door where my dad rented the rooms. He had stopped me using the house phone to ring my friend Rachel, in Sunderland, so I got my pennies together and went next door to make the call. I was leaving to go to Scarborough again the next day and the care home that my friend lived in had agreed to let Rachel come along with us. Andy came down while I was on the phone and started hanging around. I cut the call short as felt I couldn't speak while he was there listening... I was so brass to say to my friend that some dick head was hovering around trying to listen in, while that dick head was right behind me.

I put the phone down and got up to go... He stopped me. "It's only because I care about you, you know," he said.

"Fuck off! Care about me?" I answered back sarcastically.

"I do! That's why I get worried about what you're up to!" He said. I kept trying to leave but he would get in my way and keep talking. "Look, I really need to talk to you," he said. I told him that I had nothing to say to him and didn't want to hear anything he had to say, but when he kept going on and not getting out my way I told him that we would talk, but it would have to be after my holiday. I just wanted to shut him up and get him out my way. I had no intention of speaking with him when I got back.

He said this was no good and he had to speak before I went away. I told him I couldn't as I had to get back home right now as dad would be coming looking for me and the fact it was already 7pm, he wouldn't be letting me out again tonight. Then he turned. He said that I had to give him time to talk and that it was important. He said there were things he needed to tell me and explain. If I didn't give him the time he started threatening that he would be back round to see my dad that night and tell him things so bad about me that I wouldn't even be allowed on my holiday the next day. He said that if I didn't play along he could make my life very difficult... Which I didn't deny for a moment he could... He already had been, but what did he have up his sleeve next that could get me into so much trouble?

I didn't want to find out so I told him to start speaking... "Not now," he said, "your dad might come round and I need time to speak with you properly." I reminded him that I couldn't and told him to just tell me whatever it was now, but he wouldn't. He told me to sneak out when my mum and dad were asleep and come round to him. He said he would be waiting up for me outside and would let me in, then we could talk properly. I really didn't want to do this. I was petrified about the idea of getting caught... And getting caught for something I didn't even want to do in the first place... It was one thing sneaking out of a tent I wasn't even sharing with my mum... But sneaking out of the house with my mum and dad sleeping in the room next to me was something different. I felt I had no choice though. I was backed into a corner.

I did sneak out finally about 1am... thinking I'd get there and that he had been bluffing all along and I could go back home quick, before getting caught. But no... There he was waiting at the door. "I've been watching out at yours for all the lights to go out downstairs, so I knew you'd be round soon." He showed me up to his room, which I wasn't happy about. "We can't stay downstairs you might get caught! Your dad would go mad if he knew you'd been sneaking out in the night." We went into his bedroom where the first thing he did was offer me a cigarette. I was angry with him at first and quite mouthy. I told him what I thought of him and how he confused me... On the one hand if he saw me out smoking he couldn't wait to run back and tell my dad, then on the other he's offering me cigarettes himself! I got to the point where I couldn't care less anymore! So I took the cigarette.

Then however, he pulled out a bottle of poppers (something you smell that momentarily gives you a high, then leaves you with a headache). He had told my dad in the past that he suspected me taking drugs too... Which at the time was a lie and again here he was offering me this! I had done poppers before and was aware how it would make me feel so refused it at first. He started to soften in his approach to me and apologised for how he'd made me feel and how he'd acted over the last few months. Though I felt annoyed with him I appreciated his apologies and actually began to forgive him. Naively I thought we'd got it sorted and relaxed a bit having a laugh and joke. He gave me a beer which I accepted then he got the poppers out again. I watched him have it then him laughing, so I took some too. "We might as well make the most of this since you made such an effort to be here!" He giggled.

I'd been with him for about two hours. Realising the time and knowing I had to be up early to get ready to go away with my mum again, I got up. "Wait!" he said. He began to explain to me that the reason he had acted the way he had before was because he liked me so much and cared a lot about me. This started to rile me again thinking that why would he want to cause so much hurt to me if he liked me that much, it just didn't make sense... He said how jealous he got to see me hanging around with any other boys because he wanted to be with me. I started getting really nervous, almost knowing what was coming and thinking how can I wriggle out of this one? I had absolutely no attraction to him and was very aware of his age, which creeped me out a bit at this moment, him saying these things to me. Don't get me wrong... For a thirty-two year old man he was probably quite attractive, but at thirteen I just saw him as old!

I became insistent on leaving and even tried a couple of times, but he pulled me back and started turning quite nasty again... He started threatening me again with the whole telling my dad everything and even about tonight! He said that he would tell my dad that he was testing me to see if I would do it and take everything he was giving me and that I gave in to everything, showing that I obviously did these things with other people too... Then weirdly he changed again, collapsing on the bed with his head in his hands and started to cry, saying again that he was sorry and that he just liked me so much and wanted to be with me for as long as possible.

Obviously I know now that he was being extremely manipulating, but at that moment in time I was just so confused! He was saying that he knew once I'd gone tonight that I wouldn't want to spend time with him again and that he was enjoying my time so much. I began to play along, becoming wiser to what was going on so tried to reassure him that this wasn't the case, that I liked him too and that when I got back from holiday I would spend time with him... I was saying anything now just to get out of there! "No you won't!" he said... "You will be busy out with your friends and boyfriends... You won't want to spend time with me." I smiled and got up to go trying to come across very blasé saying that I definitely would and to stop being silly. As I began to open the bedroom door to leave he shot up off the bed pulled me back and started to kiss me... Again I just went along, hoping that he would just kiss me and let me go, but that wasn't the case.

The key for the bedroom door was in the lock. He closed the door and locked it... "What are you doing?" I said... "I have to go now."

"Just a bit longer," he said smiling. The more he was kissing me the more he was clearly getting turned on and all I could think of was what could I say next to leave! Everything I did say was just ignored to the point where he laid me on the bed. As soon as he did this he got up for a second, where I shot up to go to the door immediately, but he went straight to it and took the key out the door, put it in his trouser pocket then began taking off his jeans... "I'm just getting comfortable," he said smiling.

I learned later in life about a psychological experiment that took place where lots of dogs were taken, put in a pen with a metal platform then given electric shocks. Awful I know! And

I am sure wouldn't be allowed to be done today... The idea was to watch the dog's behaviour of how they reacted to continuous shocks being given. At first the dogs tried to fight it and reacted barking and trying to lift their feet from the platform... Some tried to get out of the pen the way they had been let in, but couldn't because they were locked in. The scientists were intrigued by how quickly the dogs gave in... stopped fighting it and stopped resisting it... In the end the dogs gave in and actually laid on the metal platform, just accepting the electric shocks given... Their behaviour became passive. Despite the distress the animals were clearly in, they quickly realised there was nothing they could do about it and just took it.

That's exactly what happened to me that night... I quickly realised there was nothing I could do. I was vulnerable and helpless, feeling that if I made him angry he would tell my daddy everything and start getting me into worse trouble than ever before. I became passive and just took everything that came... Two hours later, he let me go.

I got back to my own bed about 5am. Managed about an hour's sleep then was up to go to my camping holiday... The whole three days away it was going over and over in the back of my mind.... I was dreading going back to have to see him again... I prayed and prayed "Please, God, just make him go away!" I never wanted to see him again and was worried he was going to keep wanting to see me and want more from me when I got back... I was also worried that he might have said something to my dad while I was away... I really didn't know what I was going to return home to.

Thankfully when I returned home, the first thing my dad said was "You know that Andy? He's just left! Went yesterday out of the blue! He paid for the next two weeks saying that's his notice paid as he had to go quickly. That was nice of him wasn't it?"

"What gone for good?" I asked. "Where?"

"Oh far away. Don't know if we'll see him again. He seemed a bit worried and in a rush to leave. I told him not to worry about paying me the money to give his notice, but he insisted. Very nice man."

Was that his conscience speaking? Or was he getting worried of what I'd say when getting back, knowing that he'd get into a lot of trouble... Sleeping with a thirteen year old? I was so relieved to hear this news! God had heard and answered my prayers xxxxxxxxxxxxxxxx

Chapter 8

Manipulation

A few months after what had happened with Andy I was in a pub/restaurant with my dad when he pointed out a blonde haired lady just leaving... "That's Andy's ex-wife." He said "She's a cruel lady... given him a really hard time since they split up and stopped him seeing the kids and everything. He was so upset you know."

"Why would she stop him seeing the kids?" I asked, for a second feeling sorry for him. "Well... sometimes when couples split up they do that just to be nasty, but she got the police involved and everything with him."

"Why?" I asked even more interested.

"She accused him of messing about with the oldest daughter, nine years old."

"What do you mean messing about with her?" Genuinely not understanding.

"Like sexually interfering with her... She said he was also quite violent."

My blood ran cold and I felt sick... "That's horrible! Why did you let him live at yours?"

"Well I didn't really know what was going on at first, but he was the one that told me everything. None of it was true and she was a drug addict. She gave him a really hard time."

"How do you know none of it was true?" I asked.

"Well... I suppose you don't know, but I felt bad for him you know, he seemed a good man."

I remember getting up at that point, going to the toilet and actually being sick.

Growing up, my dad was best of friends with another Mauritian guy who lived in the same town as us. His kids knew my dad as a close uncle and all the kids, including me just knew each other as cousins... though there was no blood relation. For whatever reasons our dad's had a fall out when I was aged around nine or ten years old... The friendship was rekindled when I just turning fourteen years old. My uncle's kids were three years and six years older than me. The oldest one being the boy, Zac (name change). It was strange at first getting to know my lost cousins once again, as those few years we hadn't seen each other, we had all changed a lot! You do over those tender years... I myself had gone through massive changes of being known as the quiet, shy girl to this mouthy, loud couldn't care less party animal... Boy! Did my parents know it! Bless 'em... but then I guess they didn't understand the reasons behind why I was like that...

I always showed a lot of respect for the Uncle as that is how I had always been bought up to be with family, though he could be very cruel at times with me. For example... Being a teen and being very insecure about my body and appearance, he didn't help when he would make public comments about my weight or size... At that time I was a size ten, but made to feel like an elephant! I never suffered badly with spots and acne as a teen, but again whenever I would get the odd spot, I'd walk into a crowded room at his house where he would shout out "What the hell is that on your face? It looks disgusting!" I would be so embarrassed! It's no wonder his daughter suffered severely with anorexia for many years of her life.

There's a saying... "The apple never falls far from the tree." Well where his son, Zac, was concerned that phrase couldn't be true... As I was starting to find out more and more. There's times when Zac would be nice to me and give me cigarettes, maybe buy me a drink if he saw me out in the bars and make out he was looking out for me... Sounding familiar? Then there would be times he was vile towards me. He often tried to manipulate me and blackmail me into doing sexual things with him and often having sex too. He could be really forceful at times and he could be quite violent towards me... More humiliatingly in front of others too. Well you don't need to think too hard on what the threats of the blackmail may have been... As always, my dad... Trying to tear our friendship apart. Zac was very jealous of the relationship between me and my dad as his own father was so stern and dismissive. My daddy could really be just as much as a friend to me as he could a father. We could laugh and joke and I truly loved spending time with him.

Zac got into the habit of coming round to our house every day to eat with my dad, many nights of the weeks to have a drink with my dad or take him out. He loved my dad! Supposedly... However there were ulterior motives to getting in with my dad... One of them was gaining my dad's trust and manipulating my dad into believing whatever he wanted him to... This is where any dealings with me were truly to his advantage... Again I found myself in the position of being grassed on for things I hadn't done, caught out for all the things I had done (I didn't help myself) and being put down all the time for who I was turning out to be... All thanks to Zac. This sadly went on for a few years. He even started bringing friends over when he knew my dad wouldn't be in and keep a watch out downstairs while they came upstairs, raped me and left again very quickly. It was horrible to not even feel safe in my own house and never know what one hour to the next might bring. I felt I could never tell my dad any of these things as it would cause so much trouble within the family and I would be the one to look bad out of it all, somehow.

Zac had always used me as a prop to also make his current girlfriends jealous. He loved playing mind games with them. I don't even know the stories he told about me, but I know that at times... they were after me! He found this all very amusing. I think it boosted his ego and made him feel more cared for by his girlfriends to see them jealous over him. There was even a time he bought his latest girlfriend at the time to our house. She made some excuse for me and her to go upstairs to chat and get to know each other while the men chatted. She was about twenty-one years old and I was sixteen. She started off all friendly then started questioning me on Zac and previous girlfriends and that she had even heard stuff about me and him and wanted to know everything! I was very careful on what I said. Zac was someone who was safer to have as a friend than an enemy... Which I'd had to find out the hard way.

Not soon after though, Zac was getting nervous about what I might be telling her. He asked his girlfriend to go downstairs a moment while he spoke to me about something, then hit me a few times and warned me I had better be saying nice things about him as he really liked her. As much as I just wanted to hide away and cry, I had to sit with his girlfriend for another hour, plucking her eyebrows for her and saying all nice things about Zac... Lying through my teeth! Then to have her turn on me a bit with a slight threatening tone on how she's got her eye on me as well... All his girlfriends were wary of me as knew something was going on, or at least suspicious! They just didn't know exactly what was going on.

The weirdest thing about all of this, is that I actually had a soft spot for Zac... Despite all the cruelty and abuse, when I saw him genuinely down about something I empathised with him and felt for him... I'm not saying in any way of wanting to be with him... But I suppose I've always had that caring, unconditional ability to love. Despite everything, it's as if I understood him... Why he was the way he was... And I saw with compassion... Regardless of being on the receiving end of his cruelty much of the time... I had a boyfriend who I'd been with for the last two years... There's another story in itself! With a guy in his mid-twenties. The great thing about being with this guy is that he wasn't local... so I could still get about my business without worrying too much he would ever find out... And I did literally get on about my business. I lived an extremely single lifestyle, let's say... But I don't doubt he was doing the same with me. That's probably why I didn't feel bad about it.

Zac knew my boyfriend a little and seemed to get on really well with him... It was all very secretive behind my dad's back as he would flip if he ever found out. Another thing for Zac to blackmail me with. For some reason, maybe because my boyfriend wasn't local and couldn't get in the way of things, Zac didn't bother about him, as he would with any other boys he ever saw me with.

Zac had split up with his girlfriend and it seemed to hit him really bad. He seemed down a lot of the time. He started asking me out with him to go places, which he never really did before. To go shopping, out to eat, to his friend's house for drinks, parties etc... I would feel bad to say no as he would pull some kind of sob story. I was enjoying him actually being nice to me for a change. He still had his "Dick Head" moments, but overall he was being kinder. He started asking me over to his place to sleep the nights, which I did at times out of feeling sorry for him. He had his own place where his sister would often stay over too. I would have to lie to my dad that I was going to stay over with his sister. Which my dad was fine with. Sometimes Zac would go straight to my dad asking if I could stay over that night because his sister was staying, before he even came to me... Like I said... I had learned that this guy was better a friend than an enemy.

We would literally just hang out at his and when we went to bed, there was no pressure to have sex. There was a completely different side to him I was starting to see... His vulnerable side... Before going to sleep he would just ask me to hold him. I thought this weird as our relationship wasn't really affectionate and loving, but he'd get snappy if I refused... So I just held him till he fell asleep. If he would wake up and I wasn't holding him he would scurry me back over for more cuddles and just go back to sleep. In the mornings he would usually be his cold self once again, but during the night he became so childlike, vulnerable and needy. I suppose that's why I didn't mind too much about staying over sometimes. As I knew there was nothing much more behind it... Then came his twenty-first birthday.

He was having a massive party at his house for a load of friends and cousins to come over, get trashed then sleep over. Of course I had to go as my dad would have even been disappointed in me for not. As I was getting ready, taking my time, he kept ringing me. "Are you ready yet?" he kept asking. I kept telling him I was coming and that Dad would drop me off when I was ready. He was insistent that he wanted to pick me up and take me. I was in no hurry... and in fact a little miffed that I had to go as would have much preferred going out with my mates into town for the night. He ended up turning up and just sitting watching me do my last bits of make-up, hurrying me along.

On the drive to his I realised what this was all about... He felt the need for whatever reason to announce to everyone that we were a couple... "Officially." First I'd heard of it... I laughed and explained that this weird idea of his wasn't going to work because at some point, one of his friends would see me out with another guy and that I would just have to tell them that we weren't really going out... I don't know why he felt the need to lie about this to his friends, but he had... Now he needed me to step up for him regardless of everything in the past... I could have really used this to my advantage at the time, but didn't... However Karma tangled its way in there all by itself...

I agreed to play along at his party and admit to being his girlfriend to everyone that asked. Everyone kept coming up to us saying what a lovely couple we made, how lucky Zac was etc, etc... Zac was in fact treating me like the princess that night... Well I suppose he had to! Announcing me out loud to everyone that he loved me and how beautiful he thought I was... Asking people to move off chairs so I could sit down and all that... Proper laying it on! My boyfriend at the time was away in Pakistan for the month... So we thought... He'd arrived back earlier than expected, knowing Zac was having this house party... I don't know if my boyfriend had found anything out or was suspicious, but he turned up at the front door of Zac's. It was already 11pm, so this was extremely unexpected!

To make it worse, Zac and I had just gone into one of the bedrooms for a bit... literally for a chat and him thanking me on my act so far... Of course he wanted to make out to others that there was more going on in there... Someone came to the door saying who was at the door. "Shit!" Zac stressed... For a moment I was excited forgetting everything as I had missed my boyfriend. I just giggled, realising the show was over! I felt for Zac, but wasn't going to make my boyfriend feel bad. He said to let him go down first and see him, then me come in a moment so it didn't look suspicious... I waited a moment, then thought Zac might play games and tell my boyfriend I wasn't there so I hurried down to see him.

Everything was so strange that night... My boyfriend wasn't usually one to announce his love for me, or even be overly affectionate... But tonight was different... Maybe he'd missed me... He saw me coming down and shouted at the top of his voice "There's my girl!" With his arms out and gave me the biggest welcome! Zac's face just dropped... I genuinely felt for Zac, but there wasn't much I could do without making my boyfriend feel shitty and that wouldn't have been fair... My boyfriend was usually all right with people overall, but this night walked in with the biggest attitude and dominance about him that everyone just crumbled under.

I asked him if he wanted us to go for a drive just the two of us, but he said he couldn't stay long. He shook Zac's hand and wished him happy birthday then said quite bluntly to him that he was only there to see me, so no offence... He then walked into the kitchen with me, where he was just holding me and talking... It was obvious we were a couple let's say... A real couple... Everyone was looking over all confused. God knows what people thought of me! There was about twenty people in the kitchen with us and I think my boyfriend was very wary that people were looking over very confused. He ended up standing up just as Zac walked in and shouted for everyone to get out the kitchen so he could spend a little time with his girlfriend who he hasn't seen for three weeks! Zac just stood at the door looking defeated and very embarrassed and held the door open for everyone to walk out. However loving my boyfriend was being towards me that night, it was very apparent to everyone that he was ready to start something at any moment if anyone got in his way... I hadn't seen him like this before. To this day I still don't know what came over him that night?

Zac came up to my boyfriend and nervously asked if everything was alright? To which my boyfriend answered "Yes! Just fuck off and leave us alone for a bit!" Zac did as he was told. I have no idea what people were saying about the whole situation for the rest of the night. My boyfriend had been a knob to me over the couple of years we were together, but that night he really was a ray of light to rescue me from a very difficult situation...

If he hadn't have turned up, people would have still believed Zac and I were an item and I don't know how long he would have let that go on after... He would of been even more obsessive over me, controlling, scared for people to find the truth which would have made him worse with me in a threatening way. I would have had to be careful what I was doing when I was out and who with as Zac knew a lot of people... and at the end of the day... Why should I have done any of that for him... making my own life even more messed up and complicated for someone who had been so cruel to me? The only reason I was playing along as I did at first was out of fear... So my good for nothing boyfriend at the time saved me! Everyone has their uses. After he insisted on driving me home, which I happily accepted as couldn't wait to get out of there! Could the angels have played a hand in this? Hm ... We'll touch on that later ;)

Chapter 9

Escaping

I don't want this whole middle section of the book to be so dismal and just a list of rapes and traumas, so I'm not going into too much detail about the rest. I could write a whole book on that part of my life! But this book is about more than that. It's about how I came through it all... With lots of help of course from spirit, the angels and God. There were other situations similar that went on with different people and again some much older men and some ending in rape or sex of a manipulated forced nature. All where I was left feeling like the dogs on the electrified platform. The problem was, the more that happened the more rebellious I became. The more I had no care for myself or what happened to me. A defence and coping mechanism I suppose. This was all under the age of sixteen. I was known as the party animal always out and wanting to be out... The thing is, if I was home and alone I was left in my thoughts... Not a nice place to be.

I would end up out nearly every night of the week, taking pills and getting out of my face and ending up putting myself in more vulnerable and dangerous situations... I was very lucky. I would walk home alone from nightclubs at 3am, go back to different fellas' houses, and stay out at friends till 5am. During the day I just wanted to be out doing pretty much the same thing. Hanging out with different guys who were up to all sorts! I was just out to have whatever fun I could get and pass my time. What did I have to be scared of anymore? Definitely not dying... In the back of my mind I would have been grateful for that... Many times I tried to overdose with as many tablets I could find and a whole load of alcohol. It never worked though. It's as if every time someone took advantage of me once again, I became even angrier. I adopted more of a "couldn't give a fuck attitude" determined not to let those things get me down. Having sex with lots of people was partly about me showing myself that I wasn't fazed with what I'd been through. Of course that wasn't the case.

It's a strange feeling the first time it happens... You don't know how to feel about it or what's expected... I learned at that moment that you almost have to live up to what is expected of you, having been in that situation. Living up to expectation... To hear of someone being raped you instantly assume them to be messed up from it, vulnerable, frigid, scared, upset... A fear of men or having sex again. If someone claims to have been through something like this, but doesn't show the tell-tale signs of assumption, you're very likely to think there lying... Right? Could it be that so many people who have been through similar things begin to walk this very path, because it's what is expected of them. "How am I meant to feel?" many ask themselves... Well I was determined to not be this way... I was determined to NOT to be the victim! However, I know now that I was actually showing more signs of being a victim by acting like this, only on a bigger scale. I was on self-destruct mode. Nothing more dangerous than been out to get yourself, as there is no hiding.

Don't get me wrong... Inside I was feeling all those things, but I wasn't about to let anyone else see that vulnerability in me. I learned to be the fighter. Getting it on, off my own back with other guys was my way of putting two fingers up at everyone and everything that had ever happened to me in the past. It was my way of facing my fear and getting over it every time. I also didn't tell friends about any of this... Instead, sometimes I would tell them when stuff happened but put a slightly different twist on it to make it sound fun and not like it was at all! Again almost another way of convincing myself it wasn't what it really was. In all I've been raped or forced into sex by nine different guys. The hardest one that hurt the most was when my uncle raped me. This was the one I found hardest to deal with.

He was my dad's brother who lived with us for a time. I knew him more like a second father as he was always around to look after us while Mum and Dad were out working. He came to us from Mauritius when I was eight years old. He did go to live in London for a couple of years when I was eleven years and we saw him for quick visits a couple of times. He came back one particular time when I was thirteen years old to stay for a few weeks. He was in his mid-thirties I think. He had found out I smoked and would sneak me the odd cigarette. He was like a good friend to me as well and always made me feel like he was on my side, happy to help when he could...

Then one night we were celebrating my Auntie's birthday with a few drinks. Dad let me have one bottle of alco pop... but my uncle kept bringing up more drink for me. Even whiskey! Which I couldn't stand and refused to drink at first, but he kept encouraging me and saying "Come on! You better drink it now I nearly got caught bringing that up for you!" I had a king-size bed at the time and my aunty slept in the bed with me that night... There were other family staying over too so it was a squeeze where everyone slept. I remember being sick of out my bedroom window before lying down. I was in such a state. I had never touched whiskey before and at thirteen years old was probably very dangerously drunk.

Next I knew my uncle was trying to get into bed with me. I could barely move, but managed to tell him to "NO" and to go sleep somewhere else. The next thing I knew I woke up my nighty being pulled up under my arms and he was doing things to me... As the realisation hit of what was happening I froze. My body became paralysed. This has never happened to me since and has only ever happened the once to me. I don't understand to this day, but can only assume it was some form of fear and shock. Inside I was screaming for him to stop, but I couldn't speak, I was trying desperately to move, to push him away or jump up... But nothing... I just couldn't do anything. The longer this continued the more scared I became inside and panicked. Eventually the only thing I put my focus on was trying to gradually move my hand across to nudge my auntie who was fast asleep next to me.

Everyone had had a lot to drink that night and she was out for the count. It took ages but I managed to touch her arm for a moment, then my uncle noticed and pulled my arm back. I managed to murmur a couple of nos and stops but he continued. Then he moved on top of me to put his thing in me. I remember the pain and the stinging and panic rising within me as I laid there helpless. Suddenly it was as if I was lifted! And with that it gave me this sudden energy to throw my uncle off, to which I jumped quickly out of bed and to the bathroom. When I say lifted, it was literally like a hand went under my back and propelled me up so fast that my head even fell back. To have lifted myself up naturally from laying, my head would be forwards. Something lifted me! And whatever it was gave me the boost of energy that helped me get away.

My dad and other uncle were still downstairs talking so I couldn't even go get into bed with my dad to stay safe. I didn't want to get into his bed alone in case my uncle followed me in. So I had no choice but to go back in my bedroom and wake my aunty up. My uncle was pretending to be asleep on my side of the bed. I kept pushing my aunty to move over so I didn't have to be next to him and eventually she woke up. She told my uncle off for taking up room in the bed and told him to go somewhere else to sleep... Then I was able to get back into bed. I was in a state of shock for the next couple of days and began to get more and more angry towards my uncle. My attitude towards him was awful and with that he changed towards me too. Making my life difficult, bullying me, getting me into trouble with my dad, mind games blah blah blah... same old... Story of my life at that time!

He came back to live with us for some time after. I didn't tell anyone until he had gone back to live in Mauritius about a year after. I told a friend about it in confidence and had no intention of telling my dad... I knew it would break his heart and I didn't want to be the one to break his heart... But the friend I told forced me to tell him. I never forget my daddy's heart ache that day and his tears... I felt it was all my fault. I know now it wasn't but at that time the pain I felt at that moment was worse than the moment my uncle raped me.

Chapter 10

My Husband, My Saviour!

Since I was about twelve/thirteen years old I fancied the pants off a guy called Christian Rockett. I saw him one day just out and about and was quite taken by him. He never knew me, or noticed me... Thank goodness! I was just a young kid and he was five years older than me. I always knew when it was him I'd seen, because of the white patch of hair on the back of his head (he has vitiligo). I was terrible for getting people mixed up and still am now! So it was good he carried a trademark sign with him. One of my close friends big brother, was good mates with him. Sometimes she would come to school teasing me that she'd been taken swimming by her brother and his mate... Rockett! I'd get so jealous! I would say prayers to God... That were more like chatting away to an invisible being, saying "Please God... Let me meet someone who is kind to me, treats me like a lady, has respect for me and more than anything, makes me believe he loves me truly..." That would have been the cracker! Something I thought no man could ever achieve. I would say to God, "Does this kind of bloke even exist?"

In this prayer I would also say... and I quote! "My DREAM guy would be all of those things and look like Christian Rockett, but I know any half decent bloke isn't going to be good looking as well... and if there were any blokes out there like that there not going to fancy me. I will settle for an ugly bloke as long as he is loving and good to me." I was just desperate to feel loved I suppose. My mum and dad were going through some really difficult times and split up when I was fourteen years old. I stayed living with dad, but of course he had so much going on with other stuff and he got quite depressed at times too. I would pray over the years for this ideal man to come into my life to make everything better... Then one day he did.

God didn't just bring the guy I would settle for. He bought me my dream. My Christian Rockett... And guess what? He was good looking AND all of the nice things. He worshipped me, treated me like a princess and most of all... made me believe that he loved me. We'd been together about four months when we were carrying a few shopping bags home from the supermarket. Suddenly on our walk he just stopped dead in his tracks. He looked at me and said "Put down the shopping bags!" I asked why and he just insisted I put them down a moment. He was carrying the heaviest all ready, then scooped up the bags I had been carrying too. At that moment he stood there with all the bags and said "From this moment on you will never carry any shopping bags again! Not when you're with me I won't allow it! You're my lady now and I will treat you like the princess you are!" From that day on he never has let me carry any shopping bags. God even gave me my gentleman.

I was seventeen years old when I got together with my Christian. Everything seemed to be perfect timing. First of all I was of age. My boyfriend who I'd been with for nearly three years began to fizzle away into the background. We just started seeing each other less and less. I would miss his calls a lot as I was out busy getting trashed with my friends or hanging out with some other boys. I would be all over the place and would forget to ring him back. He didn't ring often anyway. About six weeks went by and I didn't see him, then we just decided to call it a day. I think he realised I was going off the rails a little and was losing interest. Three weeks later I met Christian!

It's a funny thing. When I was about ten years old me, my mum and at the time baby brother, were walking through town when a gypsy lady stopped us. She asked for a moment of our time and asked my mum if she would like to hear the future of her children. My mum tried to push along and get on with her business, telling the lady she wasn't really interested. There was something about this lady that intrigued me and I urged my mum to stop, but she ignored me... This is until the lady told my mother something to stop her in her tracks.

"This is your daughter and your baby son, but where is your other son today?" My mum stopped to ask her "How do you know I have another son?" The lady said she knew a lot more than that if my mum would give her a moment of her time. My mum was reeled in... "Go on then," she said.

The lady went on to tell my mum about certain things that were going on in her life at that time, then said the three children... One would grow up to be a bit of an entrepreneur, one a doctor of some sorts and the other would become very well known amongst many, standing on stage, but not like a pop star or what we normally see people on stage doing. Then she looked me dead in the eye with smile and said... "This girl will go on to marry the man of her dreams and one she has loved and admired from a young girl. She will grow old with this man and this man will forever love her and look after her. From the day he meets her there will be no other.".…

Well I was well excited! "Oh my Gosh!" I thought. "I'm going to marry Mark Owen!" Ha Ha!

And that's exactly what happened. Well not Mark Owen... But definitely the man of my dreams and the answer to my prayers. A man I admired and quite frankly fancied the pants off from a young age! My Christian xxxxxx

What is also very interesting is that the three things she said for me and my two brothers, actually all fall correct with me. I have tried my hand at starting a couple of businesses before and always had big ideas for things, but never followed any of these things through. The ones I did were not successful of their time. I completed a Psychology BSC Hons Degree and was only two years away from gaining the Masters, but financially I could not take this further... And to this present day part of the work I do now on my spiritual path involves standing on stages, platform and rostrums giving demonstrations of mediumship and angelic communications. I am becoming more and more known by people through my involvement with the Romford Spiritualist Church and word of mouth. Everything the lady said has come to light.

From the day me and my Christian got together on our first date, we didn't spend one full day apart. Some might say this was incredibly unhealthy, but we just simply couldn't get enough of each other and to be apart even for a short time, I felt a piece of me was missing. He was so funny! When he would work night shifts at the Rubber factory, he would get a half hour break about 2am. He would actually cycle to my home at this time, just so he could see me for ten minutes before having to cycle back and make it in time for work again... Crazy!

In the beginning when I would stay over at his place I would wake at any time of the night or morning to see him just laid, with his eyes open, looking at me... I would smile to ask what he was looking at and he would just reply "I can't stop looking at you, you're just so perfect." He made me feel so comfortable around him all the time. From never stepping foot out the house with makeup on since the age of about thirteen, I was at a stage where I didn't care so much anymore. I didn't care what anyone else thought of me, because I had all I needed with that one man. I had never met a guy that was so open with his feelings for me, so straight forward talking and not afraid to say what he thinks... This was a good thing, especially for the time of my life that we met. He made it clear from the start that he wouldn't take any shit. For the first time in my life I REALLY had to watch my back. Be wary of how I acted with others guys, etc, as everyone in the town seemed to know both me and Christian!

Words spread fast, so even if I stood innocently chatting to another guy for long, Christian would end up finding out about it. Weirdly he knew my reputation and had heard lots of stories about me from others (many which were not true), yet still wanted to be with me.

Not that I ever wanted to go with any other guy since getting with my Chris, but NOT going with another guy whilst being with Chris was actually a big thing in my life back then. He was the first man I had enough respect for to treat properly and be forever faithful to. I suppose men up till that point had never given me reason to have respect for them. Through Christian I literally opened my eyes to all the goodness that surrounded me. Without drink and drugs, the world was still a beautiful place. He helped me to build back up the courage in myself, my self-respect and my confidence.

In our first few months together I was still the crazy party animal me! Which Christian, bless his heart, was so patient with. He would go out with me when I wanted... After some persuasion... We would actually have such a good time together. We could hit the town just the two of us and have the best time! Dancing all night together, just being completely absorbed in each other. There would be other people and friends around we knew, but apart from being with my bestie occasionally, it was just me and him! Unfortunately this also showed him the not so perfect side to me too... I could be incredibly volatile with other people on a night out and ended up getting into a few fistful fights which Chris had to drag me out of. Sometimes even with men, which then Christian would end up stepping in and have to finish off.

Our nights out together became so eventful just about every time, with either me or him getting into some scrape or another, he began refusing to go out any more! He had quite a temper on him and was always very on guard of himself. He was a fighter before he met me, then felt extra on guard when we got together as he felt very protective of me. The stories he heard about me and knowing I had lots of male friends (which many were all just friends) sent him livid with anger and jealousy! Though he knew in his heart how much I loved him and would never cheat, there was always that little part of him that said "What if?" If a guy so much as stared at me for me too long, his watch would come off and he'd be straight over to 'em... He was very protective of his watch too.

Some girls may have thrived on their fellas fighting for them left, right and centre, but I can honestly say that this part of him made me cringe so much! I would always feel so bad for the other guys, except when those other guys happened to be people who had really done me harm in the past. Up until this day my Christian does not know most of what has been written in this book. When he reads the book himself will be the first he has ever known of the things I have been through... and we have now been together fourteen years. After telling him what happened with my uncle in our first year together and seeing his reaction, I chose not to tell him anymore.

Zac and his cousin soon got wind that Christian and I were together, so instantly began to work on trying to put an end to it, threatening me and to tell my dad things about us and what he was like. My dad had once said to me... "Until you are sure you want to marry a guy, only then do you ever bring him home to meet me." For some reason those words had stayed with me. I don't know if he ever meant them or not, but he was always very aware that he was raising his children in a very westernised society, therefore was very accepting of a lot of things... even if it was a battle for him at first. I do feel for my dad. I put him through so much in my reckless teenage years... And worst of it is stuff he never did find out! But as a mother now I would be scared witless to think my child would do the same! I'm talking things like going away to London for the weekend on a crazy clubbing session for three nights running, at the age of fifteen! Parents thinking we were spending the weekend with each other? How I am still alive to this day I don't know... Despite everything, I know I've also been very protected through my time.

So, for the first four months of being with Christian, I did not tell my dad. However he was getting suspicious as he would hardly see me anymore. I think my main reason was that I loved Chris so much, I thought he might show his disapproval... And I loved my dad so much! I was dreading possibly being in that position where I might be made to choose. Strangely enough I stood strong to all Zac's threats and moments of blackmail to keep his mouth shut. For the first time I didn't feel scared... And let's just say the threats and blackmail soon stopped when Chris introduced himself in person.

I quickly saw the heir of dominance Christian seemed to have amongst other men. Men literally submitted in his presence, no matter how big they were... And my Chris is not one of the tallest amongst men... quite the opposite, bless him. For a long time I didn't understand this, but I now know it was all to do with his own esteem issues and the need to protect himself and be always on guard. I'm glad to say that life has softened him somewhat now and he is not so much like this, but it was quite the blessing at that time of my life. I felt so safe being with Christian. From the moment we got together I knew no man could touch me or hurt me again... And from that day on, no man has.

Chapter 11

Twin Flames

In my more recent life, I have learned a lot about soul mates, soul groups and twin flames. From the minute I met Christian... From the minute I set eyes on him at the age of twelve, I knew he was special. There was something different about him that made him stand out from the rest of anyone I had ever met before. From the beginning of our relationship we called each other our soul mates... Even if we weren't overly clear of what that fully meant... We just knew we were meant to be.

When a person comes to this earth to spend a lifetime, they come as part of a group of twelve. You are one of these twelve. The people in your group of twelve are all people who will play some significant role in the life you are about to have on the Earth. The role they play may not always be beautiful. Some may well be quite difficult, but their role is never less just as important in helping you to learn on the Earth... And learning is what life on Earth is all about. Not everyone in this lifetime on Earth will unite with their twin flame. It is said that one becomes our twin flame when spending many lifetimes over with that one person. Getting to know each other inside out life time upon life time. Once another has reached twin flame status, it is inevitable these two will come together in the present lifetime... and that lifetime will be the last on Earth. This would mean the two souls are highly progressed in their wisdom and journey back to God. Enough has been taught from what Earthly life has to offer.

As part of a class in spiritual awareness, we embarked on a meditation to meet some of those in our soul groups. This would help us to realise those in our lives who truly were soul mates and to possibly give us a glimpse of those we haven't met yet. What a fascinating and magical journey this was. I visualised myself stood in a circle of twelve others. The others were hidden in a pod like cases/eggs. As instructed by the teacher, we went up to each one in turn and asked to see through the egg to see who was stood behind. Many people were not shown most of those stood within their pods, but I was shown all, but one. I was most surprised that my Christian was not in the first pod next to me. I thought he would be the first! I instinctively started at pod two and worked my way round in order. I was pod one. Others in the group went to random ones in no certain order.

My Christian was not shown to me until pod seven! I was even more surprised that my daughter Anisha was not shown to me until pod eight! And my Dad was pod six. I was very confused by this, as could not understand the order they appeared. The three closest people to me in my life were at the opposite end to me in my soul group! Once we all came back from our meditation, our teacher went round each person so we could share our experiences with the group. What was most interesting is that four other people in the class reported the same as me. Their closest loved ones being in the same numbered boxes and how they instinctually started from the pod next to them on the left and worked round in order. Also the people that we always felt closest to in life were the loved ones who sat in pod seven. If you imagine a clock face with the twelve numbers and imagine you are stood at number one, your direct opposite number would be seven.

It was funny to think that five of us in the group had experienced quite identical meditative experiences and that for us five our closest people in life were directly opposite, however nothing more of this coincidence was talked about in the class that night and I left still with some intrigue.

I spoke to my spirit guide on the way home in the car (as you do) questioning this occurrence. The answer I received was that me and the four others in class were towards the end of Earthly life times and that the ones who stood at number seven, for us, was our twin flames in life. She pointed out that those twin flames, for all of us had already shared a significant amount of time with us up until this point. Once the light within a soul shines so brightly to appear like flames, that life on Earth is the last. This means that all other progression will now take place in spirit world of another dimension. The soul itself is a ball of energy. With each life upon the earth that the soul encounters, the energy grows and becomes stronger. So when two souls meet at this part of their life long journey, they are two flames in one soul group. They ascend together.

So... My Christian was not only my soul mate... He is my twin flame. Xxxxxx

Some signs to look out for as to whether you are twin flames are things like, near miss encounters, sharing many coincidental similarities to one another, maybe being through similar situations, feeling the same about many different issues, having the same values and set of beliefs before even getting together, knowing the same people or having the same connections with others, yet strangely never meeting until a certain time in life, having been to many of the same places near or far. These are just a few to mention...

Christian was born in Bradford and moved to Rotherham, South Yorkshire, when he was four years old. When he was four and a half years old, I was born in the Doncaster District General Hospital, about twenty minutes' drive to where he lived. Though I lived the first eighteen years of my life in Retford, Nottinghamshire, all my mother's side of the family were in Rotherham. I would go to Rotherham most weekends to see different aunts or my grandparents. My grandparents' house was positioned next to a big field which went on for miles! These three big sandy humps which allot of motorbikers would play on were quite a central view point that the rest of the fields surrounded. This was known as "the Chittys" I do not know why.

It wasn't until Chris and I had been together a couple of years that I got talking about these fields and how I always used to go playing in there, going on adventures with my cousins, then getting lost for hours and getting told off by the adults. Also there was a climbing frame and slide near the part of the field closest to my grandparents. I think the conversation trailed along the idea of how much we were allowed out of the sight of our adult carers, considering all the stories we hear nowadays. As I started to explain the fields he realised these were the same fields he would venture into most days that also backed onto his home, but from the other side. He knew the parts of the field I spoke about, well. Yet we never met.

My mum and dad bought an elderly care Home in Rotherham, on Doncaster Road. Up the road from this care home was a massive park called "Clifton Park." I would often get taken to the home after school and some weekends if my mum and dad were short of childcare. My Dad would take me and my brothers to that park, especially if the fair was there. Christian's oldest sister lived just round the corner from this park. Chris would visit this park often, then for some time went to live with his sister. He would walk past the care home regularly going to and from this park or visiting friends close by. Another crazy thing is the that my Dad would go to the Pakistani shops for spices and certain shopping and would always park the car down one of the back streets, which is exactly where Chris's sister lived. Yet still we never met.

Christian's parents moved to Retford, where I lived, When Chris was fourteen years old. He finally came to live with them when he was sixteen years old, as wanted to finish the school he was in. Then we had best friends from the same family. I was good friends with the sister and he the older brother. I would often be at this friend's house and so would he, yet always at different times. So still, we did not meet. From the age of about twelve years old I did occasionally start seeing Christian around, as I said before... I fancied the pants off him! But he never noticed me. Not until the day we met on the bench that night, very coincidentally... And it was perfect timing for the both of us.

For a start, if I had been any younger than I was, he would not have entertained the idea of being with me at all! If I had been five minutes later to going to sit on that bench next to him, his friend would have already been to pick him up. He was at a point in life ready to leave the town and the country for good... He was searching for something, something better and yearning happiness. I was a ticking time bomb already well on the way to self-destruction. Christian was signed up to leave the country and start working for a company abroad within six weeks of us meeting. I didn't know about this until about a week after he was due to leave and he had decided to stay and be with me. He passed up a massive opportunity to escape the world he found so miserable once, to stay with me. For me, he showed me true happiness, true love, contentment and peace... Without the aid of alcohol or any illegal substances! We fast became each other's worlds. We found our homes in the hearts of each other.

There are so many reasons that my Christian could have found it so easy to just walk away from me. Yet he stayed strong and remained by my side. I would often want to go out still in our early days together, wanting to enjoy, party and have fun in the only way I knew how. Christian fast wanted to separate from that way of life, yet I would still find ways to drag him out with me occasionally. Truth be told we had some fantastic times together! We danced together all night long, made each other laugh and just enjoyed each other's company. We would start out in separate bars with our own mates, but give in within the hour and come searching for each other. We could go out just the two of us and have some of the best nights ever! The main downfall to this is that Christian would often end up in a fight with some guy or another. He was very jealous and wary of other men around me, due to the stories he had heard about me previously... That alone should have made him run a mile!

He had these weird and really gross ways of showing his love for me. Every time we went out it seemed normal that after taking an ecstasy tablet I would be sick within that half hour. Just a little, but it was kind of routine for me. This one night I remember being sick over a wall in the car park and he was holding my hair for me. Within minutes of me being sick he kissed me on the lips. Just a quick peck at first, to which I backed away and told him not to as I felt gross for him! At that and much to my resistance at first, he full on snogged me! Uurrrgghhhh!

Though Christian would give in at times and come out with me... Plus he would be pressured into going out with his friends occasionally, then like I said we would end up getting together again... He really had had enough of the whole clubbing and going out scene. Venturing into town for nights out and parties were becoming few and far between, until eventually we just stopped completely. When we moved to Essex, after one year of being together, we made a promise to each other and ourselves "no more drugs"... From that point on we haven't touched anything and I would not even be tempted to this day.

We often say that we were each other's saviours, we are so thankful that we met when we did. Not a moment later, not a moment earlier. No one has ever made me laugh as my Christian does. No one has understood me and my occasional ways as the way he does. The way he senses when I don't feel good, or the sudden just coming home from work and taking over everything, as if he knows I myself have had a hard day. When we first got together I wouldn't be seen dead without makeup! I never felt embarrassed to be without make up in front of him. He always made me feel comfortable enough to just be myself with him. We came to this relationship with our insecurities and have both had to work hard at giving that reassurance to one another along the way.

One of the biggest things that made me realise early on in our relationship that this was one special guy, is how he didn't just want to jump into bed with me! We were very intimate from the start, but sex wasn't ever an issue. It took six weeks to have sex with each other. As time went on I remember putting this to the test also. At what point would he break, or just leave me? No matter what I did, he wouldn't leave! Not that I ever did anything intentional. I'm sure you can imagine though, that for me, at that time, this meant a lot. Every guy I ever came into contact with before Christian, just seemed to want one thing. It's what I knew men to be and didn't expect any more from them then just that. Christian showed me that decent men do exist... However after that first time! We couldn't get enough of each other!! My eyes are open so much more now to the world and all beings that live within it. I know now that most men and women are on their own journeys of self-discovery. Sometimes being this way for a short time is all part of it. Most human beings have goodness in their hearts, some just make it a little harder to find.

Chapter 12

House of Horrors!

Christian and I moved to Romford, Essex with my Daddy in 2001. We had been together less than a year and Christian had no hesitation in us moving away together. We both knew it was for the best and it was definitely the right thing for both of us. A fresh start, leaving the past behind and all those that belonged with it. It was so exciting at first! Exploring the new town we lived in, taking day trips into central London, which was now only twenty minutes train ride from us. We loved it! When first walking into the house we were to stay in with my dad for the first ten months I got a completely secure feel about the place. In fact, I remember saying to my dad and Christian that I had never felt so safe in any of the houses I had lived yet. The vibrations felt fine. Even though at this point I was not aware of my potential in connecting with energies, or understood them much... I would still have some awareness in picking things up with the energy of a place.

This was most likely due to the fact that coming to Essex would have been my sixth house I would now live in. Six houses by the age of eighteen! And every single one of them I experienced many ghostly goings on. Not long before becoming spiritually awake, I had a conversation with a good friend Kim about how coincidental it was that all these houses I had lived and they all happened to have things going on. Then you would get many people who live in their houses and never experience a thing of this nature! Hmm... Coincidence? I will discuss this more later.

It didn't take long before things began change at the house on Knightsbridge. It started off with the usual goose bump feeling of feeling a presence in the room. This would only be in the front bedroom where Chris and I slept. Then the odd noise as if something was trying to catch my attention now and then... Then the real games began. Lots of things would happen which literally made me start to feel I was losing my mind. I would move something, put it down in one place, to return and it be moved. I would turn off lights to return and they be on again. All the bedroom doors had locks and keys in them as the place was previously used as a B&B. Many times I would go to leave the bedroom and the key would have turned in the lock, locking me in the room. This wasn't a problem as I would just turn the key back, unlock it and let myself out. However I would find it very strange that it locked in the first place.

Sometimes I would stand there thinking "Could I have locked it?" Maybe without realising. Then I would get so aware of it I began taking extra notice when I was going in and out the room. I confided in Christian about it and other stuff which had been happening to me, but he thought I was just being silly. At times he got quite frustrated with me about it. Everyone thought I was going a bit mad. For the first time I was made to feel that Christian wasn't on my side and it was horrible. Whatever force in the house was making all these things happen, they were only happening to me. I felt quite picked on and bullied actually... In my own home. The massively annoying thing about all this is that the things that kept happening were things that people could easily think "Oh you must have just done it without realising" etc. Odd things began to happen in a like-minded way to Chris after some time, but he would immediately think it was me.

Again not knowing of my abilities to link in with these energies, somehow I just knew that the interfering presence was a lady. I felt very much the lady that had lived here previously for many years and I just knew that the room Chris and I shared, would have been her room. Christian would say things to me like, "Why have you taken my shirt out again, I just put it away?" Or "Where's my whatever gone? Why have you moved it?" I began to get fed up of what was going on and the fact that no one believed me and would just reply "Our lady has obviously moved it." Chris would get really frustrated with me, probably thinking I was playing games with him... But it wasn't me.

After we had been there a couple of months, we had a few friends over for lunch. My dad's really. I was just upstairs putting my makeup on by the window, in the mirror. I remember looking at the window, slightly open, wishing there was some breeze as it was so hot and such a still day. The bedroom door was at the other side of the big room from me. The bed went long ways opposite to where the door was, so that the bed was side on from the bedroom door. Going by previous experiences I left the bedroom door wide open! So there could be no locking me in! One of my fears was always that one day, I would go to open the door, it be locked and the key gone! I wasn't about to risk that nightmare coming true. The shear thought of it freaked me out!

Then I heard a creek from the door. I looked in the corner of my eye, through the mirror to see the door begin to slowly close. This was a big heavy door that wasn't the kind to just close itself. There would have had to have been quite a strong wind to close it... But there was not even a breeze in the air. The minute I looked straight at the door, it stopped moving. The minute I looked back into the mirror it closed some more. I could see the door clearly through the mirror to see there was no one there. I took a deep breath and told myself not to get scared. Though there was no wind, I tried to spin some kind of logic onto the situation to reassure myself... Then the door closed properly. My heart began to beat fast. Unless being closed with some force or a slam would the door close so securely. It was as if someone had just pushed it slowly till the lever slotted into the catch. In my mind I said to whatever was out there that this time I was going to catch it out. There would be no making me second guess myself. Knowing I had not been anywhere near the door this time as it closed to, I knew there would be no way it could be locked also, without something incredibly supernatural going on.

I tried to be really brave and just carried on doing my makeup in the mirror, before it all got too much, with something falling out my wardrobe, to which I jumped up and went to leave the room, only to realise the door was locked! And my nightmare turned into reality... The key was gone... my heart was in my mouth! I panicked and I think for a moment went into shock! I couldn't even scream for my dad who was downstairs. I put my hands on my head and began to cry, then it's as if something or someone just tapped me on the shoulder and pointed to under the bed. As I looked round, where the bright sun shone into the room it caught the shimmer of silver that laid on the floor. The key was under the bed and just the back edge of it stuck out. It's a miracle to have found it! I wouldn't have thought to look there as the bed was at the other side of the room and a little distance from the door. I was relieved though... In a mad panic I unlocked the door and went running downstairs with tears in my eyes, forgetting we had visitors.

I quickly tried to compose myself and went to sit at the dining table with everyone. "Are you all right, my darling?" my dad quickly asked. I replied yes, as I didn't want to explain what had just happened with our friends being there. My dad laughed and said, "You look like you've seen a ghost!" My dad and his friends laughed, to which I burst out crying and told them everything what had just happened. For the first time my dad took me seriously. As I told the story my Dad and his friend just looked at each other with concern, probably because I was in such a state. My Dad said that he would take all the keys out the doors and keep them on him all the time. That way no one could get locked in any rooms again. I worried with this idea, thinking whether a spirit actually needed a key to lock the door... And if they locked it again, how would I get out with no key? Anyway, my Dad did just that, and I wasn't ever locked in the room again. Thankfully! That wasn't the end of it though.

Christian still wasn't too sure with the things I told him. We went away for a much needed few days break up North, visiting Chris's sister in Leeds. We arrived back in the evening having the house to ourselves that night as my dad and his partner were away. We went up to the bedroom to unpack and get bathed. Christian went downstairs to put pizza in the oven while I finished putting last bits away in the bedroom. The last thing to put away was the great big holdall bag we had taken away with us. After unpacking it, I zipped it all back up and put it in our end wardrobe. I distinctly remember doing this as I had a real job in getting it to stay in as there was so much other stuff that still hadn't been unpacked from when we moved house. I moved things around and balanced it on stuff making sure it wouldn't fall. I got so frustrated with it and was making quite allot of noise. I turned off the lights to go downstairs, making a mental note that I had turned off the lights... Just in case.

When I went downstairs Christian asked me what all the noise was, so I told him about my frustration with the holdall bag. "You should have left it for me to put away." He said. After about an hour we went back upstairs together. I walked wearily as a split second before going up the stairs I thought to myself "Now I know I put that bag in the wardrobe and turned the light off." It's as if I was expecting to see what I saw... Chris was right behind me and I walked slowly... As I got near the top of the stairs I could see that the bedroom light was on. I stopped and grabbed onto Christian telling him the light was on and that I know I turned it off! "Oh come on!" He said to me in frustration. As we reached the top I could see straight into the bedroom. The holdall bag was out of the wardrobe, wardrobe doors wide open and the great big bag laid on the middle of the bed with all the zips open again!

First of all I was shocked and for the first time Chris actually seamed spooked out, going by the conversation previously had about the bag. Secondly I was quite pissed off that I'd spent all that time and effort trying to get the bag in the wardrobe, only for someone to pull it all out again! I had even cut my finger a little on the zip, fastening it all up, for it all to be undone again! We went to bed both feeling a little spooked. It just kept going through my mind that if this ghost, or thing was strong enough to lift that great big bag! It could probably move me if it wanted, or cause allot of damage. Horrible thoughts flitted through my head as I fell to sleep that night. Two hours later I was woken up by knocking. Three knocks, a pause then three knocks again. I couldn't tell if the knocks were from the bedroom door or wooden wardrobe doors, but the knocks were coming from in the bedroom. I shook Chris to wake up. I panicked as at first as no matter how much I shook him he wouldn't wake! The knocks continued. Finally he woke up and heard the knocking for himself. He sat up on his arm looking around... Almost unsure of himself, if he did actually hear the knocks. They were loud clear knocks though. The knocking seemed to stop for a moment and Chris laid back down. "Come here." He said gesturing with his arms open. I laid in his arms. The knocks came back, but this time so loud it was as if two giant hands were going down both sides of the walls and banging! Christians grip got tighter and I pulled in really tight to him, burying my head. "It's okay, I've got you. You're safe." The knocks turned into continuous rumbles. The whole house felt like it was shaking and the banging was horrendous!

Somehow, we both fell back to sleep, which must have been within moments. I woke up in the morning and laid thinking about what had happened and how we possibly managed to fall to sleep after experiencing such horror! I finally woke Christian up and asked him if he remembered it and what he thought about it. "I thought that was a dream!" He responded. Certain spirits energies can drain from your own energy to empower their own actions. Fear emitting from your own energy can feed that of lower energy spirit, to the point of the person passing out. This is what must have happened to the both of us in this case.

We realised we had to do something. Later that day we were out together and I remembered a book I got just before moving down to Essex. Chris and I were just about all set for leaving Retford, Our old town, when I came across this book in the Oxfam Shop window. Now being in a small town and being so immature at the time and thoughtless, I wouldn't have been seen dead going into the place... I feel ashamed to say that now as my learning has bought me far since then... Never the less, I knew I had to get this book. So I sent Christian in to get it for me .It was about 50p and I had a little flick through it, but what caught my eye was that at the front of the book was a prayer... Supposedly to be said out loud three times to help spirit that was trapped on the Earth plain.

Helping them to move on, by opening a portal for them to ascend through. I remember seeing this prayer, looking at Christian and saying "We're going to need that one day." For that one reason I kept hold of the book and bought it with us to Essex. Strangely though, I forgot all about the book, until that day.

We agreed that when we got home we would sit together and read out this prayer. We felt kind of silly at first doing this, but it felt right. Just before doing this we sat giving acknowledgement to our lady spirit. I actually felt really bad for her that she was stuck here, unable to move on and began to realise that all the torment was just her way of getting my attention. She just needed my help. The prayer was only short. I instinctively knew to repeat it six times over and not just to say it the once. At that moment of saying this prayer I felt so much love and compassion towards her and we wished her well and goodbye. From that day on, there was never a sound or sight from her again. I do believe we helped her that day. The prayer went as follows...

In the name of the Holy Trinity, poor soul, rest in peace.
To whoever is with us in this room please grant eternal rest.
In the name of the Father, the son and the Holy Ghost. Amen.
(In Search of Ghosts by Ian Wilson,p3/4)

I have to say... I work very differently in helping Earth bound spirits move on now. But this book was meant to be. Everything was in perfect sequence. Without me realising it at the time, I was using my intuitive gift, communicating with spirit to a degree and keeping that open mind. As I look back to this time in my life, with my new light and knowledge I wonder who did tap me on the shoulder to direct my attention to that key under the bed that day. Was it the spirit lady? Feeling a moment of guilt as she saw my upset? Could it have been my spirit guide? Or an Angel? I don't know, but someone helped me that day. And I am most grateful.

Chapter 13

Orbs and Apports

From living at my dad's we moved around in two other flats for a while, then ended up back in one of my daddy's houses where we spent four years. My dad had bought a big three bedroomed house where he had planned to turn it into a care home, however once already buying the property certain legal requirements of room sizes, etc, changed. This meant my dad could not pursue this property as a care home so kept it for personal use. Christian and I moved in. My brother soon finished school and moved in, leaving the northern parts of Rotherham and it was a place for my youngest brother to stay when visiting. We had some good times there together. Until that is... When we bought something or someone home with us!

We used to love that TV programme "Most Haunted." I was hooked. Always trying to think real deep about it and listen to the history and stories that came through about the spirits. I loved Derek Aeorah! He actually taught a few bits on there that have stayed with me to this day. Small details on how spirit works and their ability to come back and visit as and when they want etc. It would spook me a lot though. Nowadays I wouldn't entertain this kind of programme as my understandings go so much deeper. If anything in my work now, I try to offer reassurance of the life that exists after life and to take away the fear. This particular programme didn't really give out that message.

I had not long passed my driving test and got my new car. I took up every and any opportunity to jump in it and take it for a ride! Me, my brother and Christian had been up late watching "Most Haunted" and having discussions about it, when I came up with an idea!... At 1am in the morning... Let's go for a drive! I was in a dare devil mood! "Let's go driving to a dark field and just sit there and see if we see anything!" I knew of these fields pretty much in the middle of nowhere, in Brentwood, near the Secret Bunker place, my brother and I had not long been. Well they were just as daft as me, as agreed! Boredom is never a good thing.

So we pulled up in the field, wound down the windows, turned off the engine and every now and then, turned off the headlights on the car. When we did that though it was pitch black. We were daring each other to get out the car and walk down the field a little, but none of us dared, not even together... It's as if we just sensed we were not alone. In my mind I was saying things like "It's OK you can come close, we're just here to say hello. Let me feel you." With that I put my arm out the car window and just held it there. It was a hot and very still night. When I first put my hand out I couldn't feel anything, then it's as if a vortex created around my arm and hand and a slight change in temperature... Like a breeze going around my hand in circles. This didn't frighten me one little bit. If anything it bought a smile to my face. I felt someone trying to communicate with me and they felt kind and friendly. I told my man and brother what I could feel, but they couldn't really feel anything where they were sat. I must admit also, that when I said those words out in my mind, I didn't think the spirits would here, but someone did... And responded.

Then I told the guys to call out like they did on "Most Haunted" to ask if anyone was there. Neither would at first, then my brother started speaking. He asked if there was anyone there and if there was tap once on the car or make a noise. The smallest tap was heard on the car, but it wasn't enough for us to determine if it was one of us, or another on the outside responding to our requests, so he asked again. Again there was a tap, this time a little louder. He asked it next to tap twice on the car so we knew for definite... and there it was. We all looked at each other now, starting to get a little spooked and unsure... I think we were all shocked that this was happening as we probably were not expecting anything. Then my brother got brave and said laughing, "Come on you'll have to do better than that for us to be sure!" With that, the loudest booms! On the car came. It was like two giant hands either side of the car banging and the car shook! With that I turned on the engine and put my foot down to get outta there!

We got back into the lit up areas and roads when my car suddenly did something it never had before. I had central locking that locked itself when the car got up to ten miles per hour. All the doors on my car were locked. I was doing about forty miles per hour when within two seconds all the locks came up on the doors, the lights came on in the car and my brother's door swung wide open! He had to reach out and grab it closed before driving past an island in the middle of the road. There was no way his door could have opened by itself. If it hadn't have been shut properly in the first place my car would have let me know from the start of us leaving and start alarming until it was closed properly. It was a Mercedes car and known for its safety. This had never happened before and never happened again after this night.

It was within days of this frightening event that strange goings on began happening within our home. I had felt presences there before this, being watched at times, feeling someone else walk into the room when there was no one to be seen etc., but this was different. When you felt this presence it was an instant jolt of fear that ran through you. Things started to go missing quite often, then reappear. Electrical equipment started playing up, bulbs always blowing out. There were times I woke up to my head being pressed into the pillow, with what felt like a hand over my mouth and not being able to breath, suddenly with its release I would take a big gasp for air... This time it wasn't just me that felt it and heard things... Everyone that stayed in the house did.

Despite all the scary bits in-between, there would be times that we would see clear, bright orbs moving around, yet we didn't feel the same fear with this. It was as if we picked up when different energies were around. Orbs are small balls of light, known as spirit lights. Usually they are white, however can at times appear as dark shadows. That does not mean they are anything negative. Using technology like infrared cameras etc., orbs can be picked up and recorded quite effectively. Just like that seen on episodes of "Most Haunted." I'm not sure if everyone can see orbs with their naked eyes, but I often do. At the time of this goings on Christian definitely did too. He often does now... Now that his eyes are also opened to it.

One particular time was when my youngest brother was staying over. The lights were down and we were watching some movie on the TV together. I saw three beautiful orbs bouncing around each other in a flowing sort of way, come from the kitchen door way, towards my youngest brother, then back up and into the kitchen. I nudged Christian to look and we just looked silently watching. We looked at each other for reassurance of what each other was seeing and just knew not to say anything. We didn't want to frighten my brother and felt no threat from what we were seeing. Maybe just a little excitement.

It was odd as I could feel completely fine one moment, then this wave of heaviness and fear would come upon me out of nowhere. I didn't realise it at the time, but I was obviously picking up on the entities energy. I was in the shower one evening when this wave of unknowing came over me. The shower was over the bath and the shower curtain pulled across. It was a blue PVC curtain that if you put your face right up to it you could just about see through, otherwise you might just see the outline of someone. Feeling this change in energy I shouted for Christian to come in the bathroom with me whilst I finished up. "Just a minute!" he shouted from across the landing in the bedroom. Our bedroom was down the corridor from the bathroom a bit away from it. Suddenly I realised a face in the shower curtain looking in. It was low down, just above the rim of the bath and looking up at me. As it wasn't very clear I just assumed it was Chris being a perv and carried on for a moment.

I looked again, seeing the eyes moving as I did and seeing the smirking smile, and dark hair. As he twisted his neck to look closer, the shower curtain moved inwards, to which I hit his face and told him to go away... Still thinking it was Chris. At that very moment I hit the face all the lights went out! I didn't realise this happened in the whole of the upstairs, I just thought it was the bathroom. Being afraid of the dark I screamed for Christian. The lights flickered and came back on, then I heard Christian run across the hallway landing and come to me.

"Were you just in the bedroom?" I asked.

"Yes!" He replied looking a little pale.

"The lights just flickered and went out in here!" I said.

"I know! They did the whole of upstairs!" He said out of breath.

"Are you all right?" I asked him, as he looked in shock.

"Yeah I just panicked and got a bit spooked. I heard you scream, then instantly the lights went out a moment. Are you OK?"

I told him that actually the lights went out then I screamed, but he insisted he heard me scream first, then the lights went out. Suddenly I remembered the face in the curtain and that whole moment leading up to this... "Were you watching me through the shower curtain?" He said he hadn't and had been in the bedroom the whole time. This made sense as the moment I hit the face in the curtain is the moment the lights went out and I could hear Chris's footsteps come bounding across the landing to get to me from the bedroom. "Well there was someone looking at me through the curtain for ages!" I was really spooked and uncomfortable with this. Chris had a quick scout around to make sure no one else was in the house, but there was no one to be seen.

Now clearly this is an example of a spirit energy making a very rude and disruptive nuisance of itself. This is an example of the kind of spirit you might want getting rid from your home and living space. Understandable. I didn't know this at the time, but there are people you can call in to help move on these energies and clear them... I myself am now one of them. Though I like to reassure people of the beauty that is all part of spirit life, there are darker energies out there, like this one. I say to people that we don't just leave this earth plane and become all saintly. We leave as we are and it is our free will as to whether we move on to progress or stay as we are. We have our Mother Teresas of this Earth, then our Fred Wests. You get the gist? That is why you don't mess about and play with what you don't know or understand... Just like WE did in the field that night.

As I said before, I was very aware of another energy that was in that house. I could feel the difference when it was this female kind energy, to the male sinister energy... This is all before my massive re awakening and knowing of the ability I had. Yes... I can be a bit slow... Spirit had to work REAL hard with me! Ha Ha! One night Christian and I were in bed when I became really aware of a lady walking up to the side of our bed. I told Christian who said he couldn't see anything. I told him I just knew, I could see her, but not as I could see him or anything else in the room. I described her hair style, what she was wearing in detail and the soft kind look on her face. She had quite a Victorian look about her and very smart with her black blouse coming right up her neck with a broach in the middle. Chris said should we get the book out again and say the prayer to help her move on. Instinctually, I asked her this in my thoughts and felt her words rather than heard them. "No I said, she just likes to come and visit. She used to live here. As I spoke I fell to sleep. I was in early pregnancy at this time and was *always* falling asleep! Maybe connecting for the first time so strongly to a spirit... Apart from being a child... It drained my energy somewhat. All I know is suddenly waking up ten minutes later shouting out the name "Grace!"

"What?" asked my husband a bit startled as I was just fast asleep. I sleepily gathered myself together thinking "What?" myself. I said in my head "Why did I just wake myself up shouting the name Grace? Who's Grace?" With that I heard a clear reply which reassured me to go back to sleep. "That's my name," said the lady... "Grace." I told Chris and we both smiled saying "Hello, Grace." Then went to sleep. Once we moved out the house my daddy was having building work done and the attic was cleared out. A box was found with old pictures. In a frame was one big, very old photo of a lady... Exactly as I had described Grace to look. The funny thing was that when my Dad showed me the picture that had been found, he didn't say anything about it, just "Do you recognise this lady?" To which I replied instantly.

"That's Grace."

I didn't ever feel threatened or scared when I sensed Grace's presence around me. I was quite happy for her to be there as and when she wanted. It was the others I wasn't so sure about. Now what I am about to tell you next, for years I could not work out who played this trick. It was something more like the male energy would play, but then there was not any fearful feelings around it... yet the memory never left me. Only of this very recent time was I reminded of this encounter during one of the spiritual awareness classes that I now run, to use as an example when talking about apports. I am now aware that this trick was played by dear Grace, but not as to be a nuisance, but to offer me valuable learning, which only very recently makes sense to me. Bless her.

An apport is when a physical object strangely disappears, then reappears somewhere else, with no explanations. There have been reports of things going missing for years! Then suddenly turning up in the most obvious of places that surely could not have been missed before. It was the day before I was due to go away on holiday with my girlfriend and I had been at work all day. Whilst at work I asked Christian to buy me some hairspray. I'd given him the money and told him I needed all the change as I needed every penny for my holiday spends!

I arrived home and went upstairs to pack the hairspray he said he got for me. It stood on my dresser so I picked it up and put it on top of my suitcase. I walked over to the bed to get something else, then when I turned back round I noticed the hairspray tin on the dresser again! In the same place. My instant thought was that someone or something was playing games again, but when I looked at the suitcase the hairspray I had put in was still there. I looked across again. There were two tins of hairspray! With this I went and stood at the top of the stairs telling Chris off for buying two tins when I only needed the one and the fact that it would be less money for holiday! With this lecture he shouted back up to me "I did only buy you the one you nuttter!"

"Then why are there two?" I shouted as I went back to the bedroom to fetch both to show him, only to find that there was only one again... On top of the dresser, not the suitcase. Had I caught something in mid action here?

When you think about it logically... Not that there is ANY logic with the work I do now! But when strangely goings on occur of this sorts you don't often see things floating across the room. They just disappear from one place and end up in another. What I witnessed that day was the midst of miracles. It was the teaching of this whole process... though the teachings didn't fall into place until literally last week! Thursday 8th May 2014... And that was with great help of my guides.

The world as I know it to be now is created on a mass of illusion. There are a few that are incredibly in sighted on how to manipulate certain illusions we see before us. Artists such as Dynamo or Troy for example. The fact we simply believe certain objects to be solid, or hard, means that in our reality it is! I realise this all might be getting very deep for many reading this right now, but for a few who have been given a similar insight, get where I'm going with this. Truly, the only reason it makes such sense to me now is through the guidance of my guides and angels. Some of my understandings are so deep that I don't even have the vocabulary to speak and share it properly. It is on another level, not Earthly or of human comprehension... But it's there in my deepest thoughts and understandings.

So to follow this notion of everything being an illusion... The illusion of two tins of hairspray was abled by creating a replica illusion of the hairspray, where it's energy still resided... now keep following... Everything has energy. My second book will go much deeper into all of this, but for now, try to follow... So this is why momentarily I saw two tins of hairspray. Then when the one vanished again from my suitcase and ended up sat back on my dresser, the illusion of the spray in my suitcase was disintegrated. Wiped out! Allowing the illusion of the hairspray on the dresser to become firm, hard and of physical form once again. So in affect the hairspray was vanished from one place to re appear in another. I'm sure I've lost half of you now!! Don't worry about it. One day it will make sense....

To this day I am unsure if it was coincidental that I saw what I did. I'm sure I was being played a little, by the tin of spray being moved, but was I meant to see the two tins at once? Was that how these illusions always occur, we just don't often have our eyes open to them? Or was this meant for me to witness, so that nine years later it would bring me this further understanding and teaching. I like to think that Grace was one clever lady. A clever lady with a knowing of what my future held and a knowing that what she showed me would years later be of valuable learning. Thank you, Grace.

Chapter 14

Hard Times

Having left school with nothing, I was very lucky to have been accepted onto NVQ level 2 course for Early Years Childcare and Education. We had been in Essex for a year where I was fortunate to land a job in a crèche at a local gym. I got to use the gym for free. Bonus! I realised how much I loved working with children. So much so I was willing to go back to college and study! It was just approaching that era in time where you wouldn't be allowed to work with children if you didn't have this particular qualification.

When going along to the college for the enrolment day and interviews, there were so many people in the same room who the tutors were trying to get through. I was seen for all of five minutes, then received a letter a week later to say I had been accepted and needed to go along to pay the fees for the year. It was around £650. My dad reluctantly came along with me to pay the fee for me warning me that I better stick at it and follow it through. He wasn't happy about parting with the cash as money was still very tight at that time. I handed over the forms and my dad was just about to hand the money over when the lady behind the desk spotted something on my forms.

She left us a moment to converse with other staff, to come back and say we didn't have to pay! I was only eighteen at the time, therefore entitled to free education still. What's more, is I was not even meant to be doing this NVQ course as you had to be nineteen years old to enrol, however my enrolment had already been passed and signed for. Result! The college said they had no choice but to let me do the course now. I wasn't complaining and my dad definitely wasn't! He got to keep his cash!

Go figure... Me who left school with nothing!! Did so well in my first year at college that I got awarded a scholarship to do my Level 3, so my Dad got out of paying £850 further fees! It just goes to show what potential a person can have when there heart is in it. I loved working with children and took my roles very seriously. It became my life! I even stopped smoking at the age of twenty as I didn't like the thought of young children smelling smoke on me. I landed a fantastic nannying job in West London, for a beautiful family and the money was great! I left my job here when I was six months pregnant. Pregnant with my beautiful girl. Anisha.

I hated being pregnant... and child birth was bloody painful! But oh my goodness... The overwhelming amount of love that flooded through my every cell when I held her in my arms... There are no words to describe. She was my world, my everything. To this day we have an amazing bond and not a day goes by that I don't tell her how much I love her. I suffered a little with post natal depression, but in a way that affected my strong love and attentiveness towards Anisha. I started to struggle with my weight once more.

I had the illusion in my head that she would be born and in no time I'd be back in my size six jeans. I was always in the gym before falling pregnant with Anisha and kept going through my pregnancy. Getting chance to get to the gym was a job in its self! Then the few occasions I did make it I would be shattered from sleepless nights and not have much energy to do a lot. When I did manage to lose all the weight, I was living on a handful of pumpkin seeds for lunch and a very small meal in the evening. I wasn't happy. All the skin on my tummy had gone loose from being stretched during pregnancy and no matter how much I worked out on my stomach, I couldn't get rid of the little bulge on my lower stomach. I was mortified to be looking like this at the age of twenty-three! I look back and realise how incredibly vain I was to let this take over me at the time, but it really got me down.

Anisha was just turning two years old when I had a load of corrective surgery. My dad paid for most of it, seeing how depressed the whole thing made me. I had liposuction and a minor tummy tuck. I'd had surgery on my boobs at the age of twenty-one as, had always hated the shape of my boobs from when they first developed. The surgeon noticed that after childbirth my boobs had gone a bit smaller and offered to do the surgery for free on enhancing my boobs. I would just have to pay the cost of the implants themselves. I spoke to my husband about this as I wasn't sure at first, but after his reaction to the question, "Do you think I should do it?" I accepted the offer.

I was so excited in the few months leading up to my surgery, just knowing it would all be sorted out soon. My world was just falling into place. Beautiful daughter, lovely flat and area we lived, my gorgeous husband who I would never have imagined parting with... Ever... Then three days before I was due to have all my surgery, my whole world and all I knew it to be fell apart and crumbled around me. I won't go into detail, but Christian and I very nearly split up and after this it took us nearly two years to get back on track. The year 2008 was the toughest of my life.

I had the surgery as scheduled. We were due to fly out to Spain seven weeks later for Christian and Anisha's birthdays. Anisha was born on his birthday. That holiday was tough as Christian and I were still on tenterhooks. We argued a lot. Luckily all my surgery went well and I was healed enough to fly out as planned. When I got back I found out I was pregnant. A wave of panic flooded me! I didn't tell Christian for the first three days. My instant reaction was that I can't keep it. I still wasn't allowed to work out to my full ability in the gym as my body was still recovering from all the surgery. My boobs were still very heavy and swollen and the scar across my stomach very delicate. I wasn't sure for starters if I would physically be able to carry the baby, without literally falling to pieces at the seams. Then there was the situation with me and Chris. I honestly didn't think we were even going to stay together. I was in a bad place, mentally and physically.

I had been on the pill, but had started and stopped a few times, trying to find a suitable pill for me as I kept experiencing a lot of negative side effects. I was actually taking the pill when I fell pregnant, but maybe hadn't given it long enough to take effect before having sex. Another thing, after having Anisha, I developed an allergy to latex... Had to find that out the hard way! Never in my life would I ever had thought I would be someone to ever consider abortion... And I felt so bad at the time to even think of it... But I felt it was my only option. It was the hardest decision I ever had to make in my life. It meant so much to me to be a good mum to Anisha and I feared that with the extra hormones racing and dealing with everything else in life at that moment, that I wouldn't be my best for her. There were so many reasons around why I decided to do what I did, too deep to go into now.

The day before going to the clinic I did lots of research on the development of the foetus at different stages and weeks. I found that at five weeks the foetus still had not taken form and was more like a ball of cells, all clustered together. In my mind it made it easier to cope with the idea to think of the baby as to not even to have formed yet. On the day of going to have it done I had told myself that if I was any more than five weeks, I would pull out and keep the baby no matter what it meant facing. I was five weeks exactly.

After having the abortion I felt Christian hated me for what I'd done, though he reassured me all the time this wasn't the case. It just hurt as I knew deep down he really wanted the baby. I kept having problems with the pill and in the end

Christian decided he would make it easier for me, for him to have the snip. I didn't want him to go ahead with it, purely because I still wasn't one hundred per cent sure I even wanted to be with him. For the first time in all our years together, I honestly didn't know from one month to the next if we would be together. It was an awful time of life. It took a long time to get over our hard times together. I am sad to admit that for a time I actually fell out of love with my Christian. For a long time it was like getting to know him all over again, healing deep wounds of hurt, that to be honest, if it wasn't for Anisha I would have walked away and never looked back. In our case, sticking at it for the sake of the child paid off. I did get to know him all over again. I forgave him for all the hurt and when I realised that I'd fallen in love with him all over again... I agreed to finally marrying him!

That's another story all in itself! Five years running we had planned to marry and five times over had to cancel for one reason or another... Because of other people, not each other. The final one of these times was when everything was all in motion and looking good. We said this time nothing was going to stop us! Then I found out I was pregnant with Anisha. Our wedding was booked for 24th June 2006 and her birth date was 12th June 2006... I was not daft enough to risk that one! So yet again the wedding was cancelled. Just before things blew up between me and Chris we had started talking about it again, but obviously with what happened it went completely off the cards! Marriage had always meant a lot to Christian, but I was never really that fussed about the idea. The fact I knew it meant a lot to Christian, I went along with it to make him happy. However after everything that went on and me turning round to say I would marry him was incredibly meaningful for me. It was the triumph of a milestone. A means to celebrate everything we had overcome!

The wedding day was beautiful. It was wonderful to have all the people that meant so much to me all under one roof. The day was perfect and the weather wonderful! We were so lucky. My daughter had just turned five so got to play a real part in the whole thing and hopefully will keep those memories forever. During the exchange of the rings Christian and I put a ring on her finger too. A diamond ring Christian had given me one anniversary, in our first few years together. It was a special day.

Chapter 15

Leading up to my Re-Awakening

Within two weeks of arriving back from our honeymoon I had to go into hospital to have an operation which involved removing a large cyst from one of my ovaries, the whole of one of my ovaries and part of the fallopian tube. Usually going into hospital I would be nervous and have Christian by my side the whole time. After going through child birth I think I toughened up a bit. However going into hospital bought back memories of going it alone when having all of my cosmetic surgery three years previous and going through all the trauma with Christian. It made me feel very much the need to be independent and not have to lean on anyone for support. Maybe trying to prove a point. There was a very afraid part of me on the inside though.

I made sure that Christian stayed at home to take Anisha to school and then pick her up again later. He really wanted to come with me, but I just said this way was better as it wouldn't put Anisha out so much, plus we wouldn't have to pay for parking if Daddy just dropped me off at the hospital. I was very brave. It was around this time that my real spiritual connections began to penetrate into my reality, yet this time with such comforting affects. I walked out to get into my dad's car, when I saw a hand take mine as I reached for the door handle. It was my granny. As she took my hand she smiled at me and said "You're not alone, baby, I won't leave you, don't be afraid." I got in the car smiling. My daddy asked if I was OK.

"Yes," I replied still smiling. "Granny just let me know she is with me today." He smiled and agreed saying that she would look after me and everything will be OK. "I know," I said confidently.

I had to wait on my bed for ages before being taken down! This didn't help as the anxiety started to build. I began to wish Chris was with me, comforting me. But when it all got too much my granny would appear again. Just a little smile to reassure me I wasn't alone and that I was OK. A lot of what got me through was actually chatting away to Granny in my thoughts, instinctively knowing she heard my every word. I did kick up a fuss though. The poor nurses thought I was something else! A bit of a drama queen that wanted treating like some princess! In the private hospital where I had my cosmetic surgery they were aware of my anxiety so gave me a sleeping pill to help settle me. I asked for one here... forgetting here was the NHS and everything was on a budget. They just laughed at me and said that wasn't common procedure and they would not make allowances for me.

I think the nurse felt a bit sorry for me though, as after a little while she came back with what she called "magic cream"... She said that this cream had never been used on any of their adult patients before and they only usually used it on very young children. The cream helps to numb the area where the needles from the anaesthetist would be inserted, as this was my biggest anxiety! Though it was all very patronising, I was very thankful of the "magic cream." I could hear some of the nurses outside the curtain laughing about it, but I really didn't care. I just prayed this so called "magic cream" really was magic! When going into theatre the next lot of nurses and surgeons had a good old laugh about it too when they saw the cream on my hand... But you know what... I didn't feel a thing. I reckon there's some truth in that magic cream.

The whole experience was actually quite moving. At times like this it teaches you the lengths that people around you will go, to show they care... even complete strangers. I woke up from the anaesthetic gradually, having my hair stroked by this male nurse soothing me back round. "There you go, sweetheart, that's it, you're coming back now. You're doing great, darling. Ah lovely. Look at those beautiful eyes. You've done really well. Everything went fine. That's it, darling." He was a middle-aged, white-haired man with a beard. I was so moved by his kindness and comforting words and thanked him so much. I think I even told him I loved him before I left him... But, I did. I loved him so much for having the heart to show me love and comfort at a much needed moment in my life.

As soon as they wheeled me up to the recovery suit, where visitors where strictly not allowed for hygiene reasons, I started to ask for my Christian. I realised it was 4pm and that he was most likely waiting for me on the ward I would later be placed. I'd missed him so much in my hours of need and just wanted him by my side. I kept saying this to the nurses and pestered them to find out if it he was here yet because I really wanted him. Finally they gave a call to the ward to ask if anyone was waiting. The nurse came back to reassure me that yes he was here and waiting for my return, well that was it... The thought he was in the same building and not by my side drove me crazy! I kept asking to be wheeled back up to the ward, but they said I wasn't quite stable enough to go yet and they still needed to monitor me. Nearly an hour had passed and I didn't stop pestering the nurses. They just asked me to relax and allow myself to recover properly, but I just told them I couldn't relax until I saw my husband.

What I didn't know is that Christian was kicking up a similar stink in the other side of the hospital. He was getting impatient as desperately wanted to see me and see if I was OK. He wanted to spend time with me before having to get back for Anisha. Eventually the nurses on both wards agreed to let us be together... They allowed him downstairs into the recovery suite to be by my side. Within half hour of him being by my side my blood pressure and everything else stabilised enough for me to be taken upstairs to the ward. That's all it took. The power of love.

That evening my dad came with my brother. I was so touched that my brother came. My brother who was always busy doing something or another, found the time to come visit me. He always made me smile... and laugh... In fact when I saw him walk towards my bed my reaction was said out loud... "Oh no!" I told him I'd rather he hadn't as I know what he's like and I begged him not to make me laugh. I was in so much pain and laughing would literally kill me... He only had to look at me funny and he set me off. It was great though. After all that! And there I was feeling great. I had my family around me, I was smiling, laughing! And trust me it wasn't the drugs... They were proper tight with the morphine! The nurses that tended to me throughout the night were just adorable. I felt really lucky to have been here during a time when all the staff were so nice. I'd heard lots of horror stories about that hospital, but they never report the good ones I guess. Shame.

The next day my dad took me home in the car. I was in agony! I was in the most pain since having the op, it was horrendous. I was genuinely thinking I would have to be rushed back in at some point, but I was OK. Christian slept with Anisha in her bed that night as I didn't want to risk getting knocked in the night and any movement on the bed hurt me. Everyone was asleep. I woke up feeling incredibly hot. It hurt me so much just to lift the quilt off me. I had been cut deep into my lower stomach muscles so every movement put strain onto my operated areas. I couldn't kick the quilt off my feet, which felt they were on fire, I couldn't sit up to move it with my hands and I couldn't shout Chris in case I woke Anisha. I was getting very frustrated and started to feel somewhat sorry for myself and very helpless.

I had to get the quilt off me so in one last attempt I managed to sit up to do so... Oh my goodness! Did I suffer after though! I laid there alone, in agony and burning up. I began to cry, tears streaming down my face, then lights in the hallway caught my attention. I looked out the open door, which I could see from where I was laid on my bed. The lights became many until I saw so clearly... My granny. She smiled at me and began to walk towards me, smiling, hushing my cries with her finger to her lips. In her thoughts she was telling me everything was OK and she will help me and make me better. As she got to my bed side she disappeared, then I began to feel like a vortex of freezing cold air begin to circle around my feet. It was a hot summer's night and there was no breeze. Granny was helping to cool me down. I thanked her over and over amidst my tears of love and gratitude. She soothed me and within moments all my pain went away and I was fast asleep.

Despite all my experiences in the past, I had no fear seeing my granny. I was in a place of complete love, comfort and contentment. I was soon on the road to recovery. From then and over the next few months following, life was on a spiralling downfall. Whilst being at university the previous three years we were largely getting by on my student loans and grants. When they stopped just before the wedding, we had worked out we should just about get by, as long as I had found a job by October at the latest. As that deadline drew closer, we were getting more and more behind in bills and there was no hope of me getting a job. This was 2011 where the economy was rock bottom. Jobs were few and the few available had so many applying for them I had no chance. I even got asked for previous experience on delivering people's ironing! That's how ridiculous it got. Employers could be extra picky of who they took on for the most simple of jobs.

Lots of things went wrong for us in that few months and the fear of losing our home of six years, where Anisha had always known as her home, was fast becoming a reality. I remember up to a year before this happening having nightmares that we lost everything, then waking feeling so relieved it was just a dream. I kept just waiting to wake up from this nightmare, but that never happened. This nightmare had become my reality. The months leading up to this point we had always managed to pay our rent, however sometimes we were a bit late. The landlords had always been very understanding of this and our position and didn't mind as long as the rent was paid by the end of the month. When we got to a point where we could no longer pay our rent I felt terrible and knew that was the point we had no choice but to leave. The landlords had always been so good to us in the past and I didn't want to take the micky by staying there and not paying up.

I sent an email to the landlady giving our one month's notice, explaining our position and how sorry we were to be having to leave and I asked if our deposit could be used for the final month's rent we were unable to pay. She said she would be sorry for us to leave and accepted the offer we made for the last month's rent. However one week after moving house she turned on us, demanding the last month's rent, money to change the carpets and have the place professionally cleaned and re painted. I felt really upset over the whole situation. I had always got on well with the landlady and her family, so this was a real kick in the teeth. I had loved my home and always looked after it well. Out of my own pocket I had re-painted and changed the carpets three times over. I was very house proud, despite not owning the property. This had been the first place in many years that really felt like home. It WAS my home. She was demanding well over £1000 which clearly I could not afford. The case ended up going to court to add to further distress over the following months.

We were very lucky to have had another place to move to. However it was a huge step down to what we had lived in for the last six years. My dad owned a house which he rented out as shared occupancy. At the back of the house my brother occupied a small one bed flat. He moved out into a room upstairs, so me, Christian and Anisha could move in. It was dreadful. It was damp, dirty, incredibly small and to top it we had ant infestations and mice! My dad was at a really low point financially and couldn't help us any more than putting the roof over our heads... Which despite its state, we were very grateful for. Our intentions were to save money to slowly pay off debt, then save to move out again, closer to my daughter's school. This also bought me more time to find a job. We didn't want to waste money on buying paint to decorate or do anything to the place. Our aim was to move out as quickly as possible. We ended up there for nearly two years.

Within this time I went through one of the biggest transitions of my life! Going from lady muck who wouldn't think twice about spending £100 on a top or £300 on a purse, I went to the poorest of people to live in the UK, many times not even having a pound in my purse to buy one small bit of food. We were so lucky for my daddy who would cook for us every day, still making sure me and my little family ate well, if nothing else. He would go to the small Tesco over the road at a certain time to buy whatever they had on offer and come to us about 8pm most evenings with his bag of goodies. Cream cakes for 10p, bags of veg for 50p etc... He carried us through our hardest times, bless him. Being a mother and to be in this position I felt I had failed my baby and my family massively. I felt guilty for all the upheaval in my daughter's life, but I tried so hard to make the best of what little we did have, for her sake. She was my strength to keep me going.

The three of us shared our one bedroom. Christian on the floor on a mattress and me and Anisha in her double bed. There wasn't much space for Anisha's toys, but we tried to make the best of the small space we had. I remember walking around the "Range" shop with Christian one day, just passing time... and going into a panic attack. My breathing got faster and my chest tighter. I went into a complete shock mode wanting to cry, yet being in so much of a state, and not being able to cry. At that moment I truly begged for the ground to just open and completely swallow me up, putting an end to everything. If it wasn't for Anisha those suicidal thoughts would have truly taken over me once more in my life.

From Anisha being a baby we had friends over all the time. Happy to have Anisha's friends over to play for the day, my friends popping in and out. In our new place there was barely room for ourselves and it wasn't the nicest of places for anyone to have to sit in. For nearly two years Anisha couldn't have friends over to play anymore. Life completely changed for us all. I got so desperate for clothes after nearly two years of not buying any clothes for myself that I had no choice but to go to the charity shops. That's when it really hit me. I went to a charity shop in Hornchurch, first of all being pleasantly surprised by some of the lovely things I was seeing... Then I looked at the prices. I fought hard to keep the tears back as I stood in this charity shop, still not being able to afford anything. The prices were far more than I expected for a charity shop, some items well over £10. There I was, a charity case myself, not being able to get anything in a charity shop!

To top it all off things got so desperate for my dad that he had to put up the house for sale. People would have to walk through our shambles of a flat to view. We didn't know from one week to the next if we would have a roof over our heads! Most of our furniture and belongings were kept in the garage as they couldn't fit in the house. The whole moving house in the first place was terrible and exhausting! Especially as it was such a sad move and lacking the excitement of moving on anywhere better. We lived with the anxious stress of possibly having to move again for a short few months until Dad's money came through for the sale of the house and us getting some place better. There was so much other stresses going on around us as well as our living conditions. Debt collectors on our backs, court summons, threatening calls. It was a very difficult time.

I was stripped of everything. I felt I had lost my identity. Soonita who was always known for her nice clothes, her style and fashion sense. The sociable Soonita who enjoyed lunching with friends, taking the kids nice places, going on holidays! It was all gone. It got to a point where for nearly a year I wore the same few outfits over and over again. Outfits which were looking worn and tatty. I had no money to even consider to buy any clothes for myself as food was always the biggest priority... I always made sure Anisha didn't go without, but even the clothes we could afford for her went downhill. She ruined them in moments anyway being the complete tomboy she is.

Losing everything I thought I was, gave me no choice to dig deeper on who I really was. And if nothing else came from this difficult time, then that gift was it. Not having the choice to try to live up to certain standards, to try and match what others thought was being a good mother, being a yummy respectable mummy who could look good, keep the kids happy and home perfect. Doing fabulous exciting things with the kids, going out with friends! The choice of all that was denied of me. My girl stayed happy throughout these difficult times and didn't go without anything. I realised the biggest gift I could give her...was me. My total self and complete love. Realising there was nothing more we could do to change our position at the time, made me realise that I just had to get used to it and cope. I realised that it was down to me to make the best of these situations and I realised, I didn't like to be sad and unhappy. That wasn't me.

I did start to adapt and get on with life as it was. I took each day as it came and moment as it passed. I began to see the simple beauties in everything, to appreciate the everyday things and sights around me. I was thankful for every meal, every moment of laughter to leave me, every smile to touch up on my lips. With every happy moment spent in that small dingy flat, I realised more and more the true importance in life. The things that made me the happiest. My family. My friends became so much more important to me. All I believed to be my identity before, was all so materialistic. Despite the small flat and its shabby appearance, it became my home... Why? Because I realised that home truly is where the heart is... And my heart was with my family. Where they were, is where I was and where I was happy. I found my identity again, only this time I found my true identity... Love.

Chapter 16

My Re-Awakening

One lady who taught me so much through my hardest and lowest times was a neighbour from our old flat. I called her Nana, as she really was what I thought all a nana to be. I didn't really have much of a relationship with my grandparents in this country. Though I love them very much. I hung out with her quite a lot, every week. She was like a best friend and my Nana all in one. My eighty-four year old bestie! She has been through some incredibly difficult times and suffered in the past financially also. She had wonderful tips to help me through and would take me out for lunches and little day trips to quaint pretty towns and villages, in return for being her chauffer or running certain errands for her. Though I was never comfortable of accepting anything back in return for the things I did for her, I know these small rewards were as much for her as they were for me, bless her. I enjoyed much of my time with her, listening to stories of the war or her parents and grandparents. I love history!

We will call her Nana G. Though Nana G was not heavily into spiritualism, mediums and all that psychic jazz... She had a small interest. We had shared odd stories and experiences we had both had in our pasts, where ghosties and strange phenomena took place. One day, a couple of months after me moving into the dingy small flat, I was speaking to Nana G on the phone. She was telling me of a book she had just read in one weekend. "I just couldn't put it down!" she said, obviously quite blown away from it. She told me how her mother had given it to her to read some thirty years previous and only now she had taken the time to read it. "Well," she said, "when your elderly mother gives you a book to read you don't imagine you would be that interested in it." The book had been sat in that draw the whole time. She decided to clear out some drawers and cupboards, came across it and thought she would give the first couple of chapters a go.

One fully read book later, she calls me with the news! "You must read it!" she said. "I just know you will like it and you will be surprised, I think you will connect with a lot of it too." The very next day she passed the book onto me. Despite her comments guess what? Well... Well when your elderly Nana gives you a book to read, you don't imagine you would be interested in it... That book sat on my desk for six months before I picked it up to read. I'll just give the first couple of chapters a read... Wink Wink! Could not put it down! It took me a little longer to read with my busy schedule, two dogs and a child look after... Five days!

The book was by Doris Stokes, *Voices in My Ear*. It was the life story of a spiritual medium. Despite the difference in years, much of her experiences in life connecting to spirit occurrences and knowings of certain things etc., were very similar to my own. As I read brief descriptions of her meditating, communicating with spirit, connecting with her spirit guide, it all just sounded very familiar. Like I knew exactly what she was talking about and understood exactly what to do as if it was second nature to me. This is why I have called this chapter "My Re-Awakening". The soul never forgets. Our mind and thoughts may be wiped of certain memories from past lives or life in the world of spirit, or heaven, which ever you may call it... But the soul remembers all. That is why you may learn something that is easy for you to comprehend, as if second nature, you may meet someone who you feel all too familiar with even though you only just met, or be some place for the first time, yet feel you have been there before. Your soul is remembering, this is nothing new to you.

Before reading this book, I had always been very aware of spirit, but also been very afraid. It is natural to be afraid of something or someone you do not understand, naturally. It is the main reason so many prejudices occur amongst man. Fear and lack of understanding. Reading this book bought me comfort. It made me realise that people in the spirit world were just that... people... Just living on the next plain, the next level on from this life. It took away my fear. I actually felt quite guilty thinking back over past experiences I'd had and all the spirits clearly trying to make contact with me. They were obviously doing so for a reason and I just told them to go away! Before I was even half way through the book, I had already made my mind up that I was going to start meditating and connecting, firstly with my guide, then see what else came. I insisted on finishing the book first though.

The strangest thing happened to me whilst reading the book. At the time it was strange, however it all made sense in the end. From the first day of starting the book I felt a strong presence, like someone watching me. This wasn't just when reading the book. I might be in the small kitchen or watching TV and the presence was always there. I would be driving in the car and feel as if there was someone in the back seat, but as if there was some kind of barrier between us. I kept going over words from the book and reassuring myself there was nothing to be afraid of. On the second day of reading the book I went to bed that night and could see the silhouette of a women with a long cloak and scarf over her head, standing on the other side of the bedroom door. The bedroom door had a frosted glass panel in it so you could see through and we always kept the light on outside the door, to shed a little light into the bedroom. The lady just stood, looking in through the glass as if patiently waiting for something. I knew she was there for me and watching me. I tried not to be scared and just turned over to go to sleep. I wasn't quite ready to connect just yet.

The next day I remember three separate times of getting into the car to go out, singing some tune in my head, turning on the radio and that song playing, not only the song I had been singing, but it would start wherever I left off! Lots of little psychic occurrences like that began to happen the next couple of days... Almost like life and other existences around me were trying teach me something, show me something, prove something to me. The third night of reading the book I got into bed. My husband and daughter already fast asleep next to me. As I closed my eyes I saw in my mind's eye a vision of this lady stood at my bedroom door once again. It startled me a little. I hesitated to look at the door to see if she was there again on this night... Sure enough, she was there. Strangely though on this night I felt comforted by her presence and just went straight to sleep.

The fourth night I went to bed and there she was again, only this time her presence was stronger. She wasn't just a silhouette. She appeared so solid in form, just like any other person would appear standing at the door and looking through the glass. It's as if the lights around her were tinted pink and I could make out ripples in her clothing, a softness in her face and a beauty and grace I had never seen before. I fell to sleep peacefully with her watching over me. The next day, I sat alone in the flat and finished the rest of the book. I sat back into the corner of the sofa with the immediate intention to meditate and try to connect with my guide. I took a deep breath and closed my eyes ready. What I saw immediately shocked my eyes to open with a start!

From where I was sat and facing, I could see through to the kitchen window. This window was quite raised up from the floor outside, so if anyone was stood at it you would only just see their head. As I closed my eyes the image of the lady appeared to be stood at the kitchen window, from the waist up, on the outside, looking in. The same lady from my previous evenings watching me. I opened my eyes to see her stood there, exactly as I had seen her with my eyes closed. I could not see her face clearly as the scarf draped around her head shadowed it, but she wore a dark blue gown and had pink lights emanating from her. I knew I had to carry on with what I was doing for this all to make sense, so I took another deep breath, closed my eyes and carried on.

With my eyes closed I could still see the lady stood at the window. I called upon my spirit guide asking them to draw upon right by my side. I heard the words come to me, "Are you ready now to let me in?" to which I responded to immediately replying, "Yes. I am ready now to let you in." I spoke within my thoughts, instinctually knowing they could be heard. With this the lady who had been on the other side of the glass for the last few days, so gracefully floated through and slowly glided towards me. What happened next was truly one of THE most beautiful experiences of my life... I had my hands rested upon my legs and loosely together. I felt the physical presence of this lady coming towards me as well as seeing her in my mind's eye. Then I felt her come face to face with me. I could feel the breeze of her breath touch upon my face and an overwhelming feeling of pure love. The energy of this presence rippled through me like thick electricity. I physically felt the lady stroke the hair from my face, then embrace both her hands around mine, slowly placing her fingers into my palms, and then gliding them away.

I asked her in my thoughts "Are you my guide?" To which she replied with no hesitation, "I am yours... I love you my child." She then began to show me images within my closed eyes. I saw myself stood within what looked like a cardboard box, in which the walls became thicker and thicker and concrete, then one by one, each wall fell down, the box began to open until there were no more walls around me. As the last wall fell she said "You see all that time you kept me out creating a barrier from me and the others." Then she smiled, held my hands once more and said "Thank you... Now you have let me in and in your heart I will stay." I became very emotional with this whole experience and the beautiful presence and words and began to cry. I promised my guide this would be forever more and I will always cherish her and hold her close. I asked for her name for whenever I may call upon her and she gave only... Mary.

As the days went on, Mary was fast becoming a massive part of my everyday life. I might be sat on the train alone, yet deep in conversation with my Mary. My knowledge was building fast and I was gaining deeper understandings about everything and everyone. I was quick to spot different teachings that came my way and was grateful for each and every one of them. One day I had to pop into town to get something or other. It was a freezing cold day, the wind was blowing and as luck should have it, the minute I stepped out the door it began to rain. I was angry that I had to go out in this weather, angry at the weather and just feeling a little frustrated with life itself at that point. No hope down the line to look forward to in getting out the mess we were in and living in... Yes... Feeling quite sorry for myself.

As I walked in my angry state I came round the corner to enter the passage way which led into the High Street. I called out to Mary in my thoughts. "Urrgh! Why, Mary? I hate feeling like this!" As ever, my dear sweet Mary responded instantly, with her gentle loving voice. "Look up, my child.

Look around you." I did straight away. As I turned my head,
sat outside some shops was a young homeless man. He was
wrapped in a sleeping bag, cold and shivering. He must have
been soaked through. A kick to the stomach hit me with a
thud and a lump rose into my throat and tears filled my eyes.
There I was moaning and angry about having to be out in this
weather, knowing that as soon as I got home I could warm up
in the heat of my radiators with a hot mug of tea... Then
there this man was... Did he have anywhere to go home to?
Anywhere to go dry off? Warm up? Probably not.

A wave of guilt washed over me and I vowed then to never
allow myself to get so frustrated over something so ridiculous
again! Out of respect for all those that suffer far worse than
me, I had to be strong, get on with my life being grateful for
everything I have in it. I may not have much and to some
may have looked very poor with our living circumstances,
but to others I may seem rich beyond words. I began to see
life very different at that point. The key to my happiness was
to see for myself that I truly was rich beyond words. I had a
roof over my head, food in mine and my family's mouths...
We had each other. On the way home from town I gave that
man the last few pennies I had left. About £2.30. When I got
home I made a hot drink, dried off and sat in front of the
radiator deep in thought and for the first time. So grateful for
my home. I gazed around at the grubby walls, the shower
curtain pole that had fallen down, plaster flaking from the
small kitchen's walls... With the biggest smile on my face. A
smile of contentment.

My two special friends, Kim and Tommy, whom I worked with for a while in youth work, were very excited to hear of my developments in my newly realised abilities. I came to meet these guys just a few months in all of this exploding for me. Strangely they both had gifts of these sorts. Both were from backgrounds of Romany Gypsies where psychic abilities, tarot cards and talking to the dead were common practice within their past communities. I was intrigued by their stories and readings they themselves would give me. I would keep them very informed with all I did, all I received and so on. Remembering how effective the crystal ball had been for me when younger, I invested in one again. I used this as my form of meditating as it gave me something to keep my focus on. I would see many meaningful images in the ball, then ask my guide questions on what I was seeing. She would inform me briefly. I wouldn't see spirit in my ball, only images of people in the present or snippets of the future that may trigger me to enquire about a relative. Sometimes certain knowings would just come.

After a session on the crystal ball I felt my granddad was not too well and was told that one of my cousins in Devon was pregnant. I rang my mum to find out. Granddad had indeed been ill and had spent some time in hospital. I asked about my cousin in Devon, being very specific on which one I thought it was, but she did not know of this. Two days later she rang me to tell me of the conversation she had just had with my aunty in Devon... The cousin's mum. "I asked her if J was pregnant and she was shocked at how I could have known, as no one knows yet except J and the mum. She was only a couple of months gone and was waiting to be clear of the three month mark before telling people." This was great evidence for my mum and she too was very excited for me.

One day I went into work and saw my Kim and Tommy. Kim came over to suggest I go to a spiritualist church. I had never heard of this before and didn't have a clue what went on. All I knew is church really wasn't my thing. Though in my heart I have always had a close and personal relationship with God, I never felt the need to follow any certain rituals such as having to go to church every week. I instinctively knew that my God loved me no matter what and I didn't have to prove anything to him. I have never been the religious type, however somehow seemed to gain certain knowledge's along the way, or instinctually knew certain things. Things that just made common logic to me, I suppose, things I didn't even think to question no matter what others might have said. Kim explained to me what goes on in the spiritualist churches and that it would be good for me to go along and watch the different mediums working and see how they do work in giving their readings, etc.

I was very intrigued by what she told me and as luck should have it, there was a church just five minutes' walk from me. Kim told me I would go along a few times, then be taken under someone's wing and that they would help me learn more. I loved going to the Church, listening to the addresses of different mediums, then there demonstrations of spirit communications. In their addresses some would tell their story how they got into this work, some would give uplifting stories and others would pass on wonderful teachings. During the service it was nice to also reflect on the week passed, give thoughts to events going on around the world and sent out thoughts to people struggling or hurt.

Sure enough on my third week of going to the church a women approached me about possibly going into a development circle that she was a part of. I was accepted into the group and so trotted along every Thursday evening. I learnt how to meditate and a couple of methods of sending distance healing and giving direct healing. Once learning the true art of connecting through meditation is when I began to excel. This was all in two months of reading the Doris Stokes book. It's as if my journey had been mapped out for me and one thing would fall onto the doors of another, when that door opened I was taken to another and so on. Within six months of my Awakening, I was on platform giving readings to my first audience, which was a true success. That moment was a tester to myself and to everyone else as I honestly didn't know how I would be, if I would get anything or anyone through. To this day I think that actually. Whenever I'm about to work with an audience, you just never know... I let spirit and the angels lead the way... I just have to have to trust.

Chapter 17

Babies in Heaven

On my second or third time at the circle, I received a reading from one of the other ladies in the group. She told me my granny was coming through and had a little boy with her. My heart sank instantly. When I had the abortion I instinctively knew I was carrying a boy. I knew the boy my granny had with her was my little boy. My son. She said the boy looked about two years old, which at the time would have been correct as it was two years later of me having the abortion. In my thoughts my mind went into overdrive with panic and guilt to which I began to speak directly to my granny in my thoughts, whilst the lady was still giving me my reading.

You see, less than three months before falling pregnant with Anisha, I lost a baby through miscarriage. I did not know at the time I was pregnant until the big bleed began and the incredible pain set in. Not knowing I was pregnant I took tablets to relieve the pain, to no avail. Going into the second day of this agony I had what felt like a massive blood clot come through me. I ran to the toilet feeling as though a mass amount of blood was about to come through. As I sat on the toilet, the clot seemed stuck at the entrance inside me. I got tissue to try and wipe it away and help it out. The clot released onto the tissue. It wasn't a blood clot, it was the perfect part formed foetus of my baby within its clear sack. You could see the head, the stump for arms to start forming and the black dots where eyes were placed.

I stared at it for a moment, not wanting to believe what I was seeing, then in a panic I screamed for Christian. He looked at it knowing straight away. It's as if we both could not admit it to each other what was happening, until after all the tests, the doctor confirmed it. I was eight weeks pregnant. I felt a terrible loss. I didn't know how to feel. It seemed almost crazy mourning over the loss of a life I knew nothing about. But I couldn't help it. I felt guilty and blamed myself allot. I thought maybe I had helped to cause it as was in the gym so much, ignoring pains in my body and just getting on with it. During that time of pregnancy I had been to Alton Towers and going on all the massive roller-coasters. I was sure all this would not have been good for the baby. I knew from the minute I had lost a girl. It was something so concrete in my thoughts, there was no doubt.

Having to go back to the hospital for more checks a few weeks later I read that for people who had lost, it sometimes helped to give the lost baby a name. The minute I saw that, the name Angel came to me. Later that day I said to Chris. "I don't know why? I just know that our baby was a girl, can we call her Angel?" Chris said every time he had thought of our baby in heaven he referred to it as Angel, so agreed to the name whole heartedly. Every year on the anniversary of her leaving us we gave out our thoughts and prayers to her. I said from the start that she would be with my granny and that there was no better person I would want to look after my baby. We did this every year, until I had the abortion three years later.

Having the abortion made me feel I had no rights to think of my Angel anymore. I felt guilty to think about her, to light a candle or even give thought to her on her anniversary. What right did I have? How can I be this way with one child to ignore the other? And how could I show love and respect to a baby I had killed and wiped away from this Earth. I felt very confused about this for a long time and coped by trying just to not think about them. I did not ever regret the choice I made with the abortion, as I know at that time there was no other option and that life could not have turned out to be as it had if we had made different choices at the time. I was good at putting it out my head until Christian spoke of them.

Every time Chris mentioned them, my blood boiled with anger towards him. He was making me face something I was trying to keep out my thoughts. He would speak of them so lovingly and I would think... How can you think that after what we did? He would talk a lot about getting tattoos to represent his two babies in heaven. I would go mad at the idea, calling him a hypocrite and accusing him of just wanting something on him permanently that would be rubbing it in my face every day of what I did. I just felt so confused about the whole thing!

Then that moment came when my granny brought my son through, sat in the circle. The messages were of reassurance, that there is no need to feel guilty for anything, it was meant to be this way. The lady told me how my little boy loved me very much and enjoys being close to me and watching me with my daughter. In my thoughts I was crying out to my little boy "I'm so sorry, baby! I'm so sorry! I've denied you all this time and I'm so sorry! I love you so much, my baby. I'm so sorry." In my thoughts I was saying this over and over, knowing my baby could hear me. In the physical form I sat there a crying sobbing mess. In a panic I called out to my granny, "I never named him, granny! I named my baby girl Angel, but I never gave him a name! What do you call him?" I saw my granny's face in my mind's eye smile and she replied only, "Star."

From that moment on my whole life changed. I fully accepted that I had two babies in the heavens which I loved so very much and knew that they loved me. My Star and Angel. Christian and I were able to talk openly about them to each other, without arguments and silly insecurities. I thought and still think about them so much and have had the privilege of seeing them often or being able to talk to them. This is a gift shared with my husband as the magical messages that come through for him are of complete love and upliftment. They are a part of us and our daughter, Anisha and we love them as we do each other. They are our family, who we know that one day we will all be together in life once more.

Now here's a gift to share with all... A gift of the truth for all to hear.

What I share with you now is for all mothers who have lost or chosen for whatever reasons to make the difficult choice of abortion. These teachings I share have been given to me directly from the Great Spirit, my guides and the Angels, so I ask that you open your hearts and minds to this precious gift of knowledge... Our babies are not placed with us, they choose us. They choose from across the lands of all mankind to have "us" as their parents. They come to us with love and all they wish to receive in return *is* love. When that child comes into our lives, enters into our physical being (womb) it knows already whether it is to touch upon the Earth. The baby has pre-chosen its path, whether that be a very short stay or a stay of a life time. What is important, that the child chose to be placed within that family. Most of us who have lost through miscarriage, or still born, will still hold a very special place in our hearts for that baby in the heavens. That love is still being received by the child and helping them to *be* and live on in spirit. For some who have chosen to prevent the life taking place on the Earth, they may find it harder to send out this love to their babies, as just like I did, they feel shame in doing so. Lose that shame and lose that guilt. It is not only me, but the angels and all of your babies that ask this of you.

There are many babies that have come to this Earth in very sad circumstances. Abuse, torture, neglect. They may have lived very short lives upon the Earth and died as a result of the lack of love they received. These babies and toddlers go back into the world of spirit. They may not want or need to come back to the Earth to live up on it once more in human form, but wish only for the love they lacked when being in human form. They often choose the arms of a mother or family where love flows freely and runs deep throughout and within. This is the place they choose to be a part of forever more, resting within the hearts and love that you and your family give. So be grateful that this child chose you... and be proud. You are their mother and *they* are forever yours.

Chapter 18

Spirits at Work

Funny how spirit works... Three days ago I did readings for a couple of friends. One of the ladies was actually more a friend of Kim's who was originally coming anyway. When I first started out giving people proper readings I would really enjoy giving readings to people I didn't t know, or know well, as I would find this more evidence for myself and my abilities. Believe it or not, I find what I do quite incredible myself and I used to really question myself. Oh could I have known that? Was that my own head working that out about the person? I'm a psychologist you see. I have a degree in the science of the mind and naturally question lots of phenomena. Like why a person may act the way they do, feel the way they do and even think the way they do. Don't get me wrong. Having this psychological knowledge does help me in my spiritual work as you tend to hit on a lot of raw emotion, so I'm better equipped to deal with that I guess, and show empathy and understanding.

But please do not think for one minute that in any way when I'm giving readings to people that I read their body language and analyse what their saying to give them readings... Cold reading I think is what that is called. Exactly what my brother thinks of people like me. Mediums, physics, fortune tellers etc... I'm sure there are some phoneys out there, but I definitely am not one of them and anyone who has had a reading given by me would tell you exactly that. The kind of information I forward could not be known otherwise, rather than spirit forwarding it to me.

"How do you know all this stuff?" One friend said to me, when I was giving her a reading. "I don't, honey," I said. "Your aunty is telling me." Obviously I meant the aunty in spirit who had flown in at that time to give words of understanding, empathy, guidance and love to her niece. Sometimes if a relative has come through, whom the person I am giving a reading does not know of (Maybe for reasons that this relative was before their time, or too young to remember when they passed away) the spirit will provide other evidence so they can be accepted by the receiver. In many cases this will be done by showing me a memory of the receiver, or a house they used to live. Anything just to provide some evidence that this spirit knows the person well enough and that they care and have been watching over them. In this particular case the "spirit aunty" described scenes from the receiver's life over the last two weeks and how all of this has been making the receiver feel. Everything I forwarded to the receiver was very personal and she had not confided in anyone about these feelings and what had been going on. Details that are so personal I could not have known in any other way possible... "Unless I had the Men in Black working for me!"

So... Kim and her friend came to visit and have a reading... This was the last week of January 2013 and Kim had a belated Christmas card to pass onto me from her great aunty, whom I'd given a reading to a couple of months previously. At the time the aunt was insisting on trying to give me £10 for the reading, but I refused. Not only did I feel terrible for taking money from such a dear old lady... I was still very adamant at this time I would not charge for giving readings. I sneakily left the money on her coffee table as I went to leave, as she wasn't taking no for an answer. I opened the card Kim gave me and there was the £10. "Tell your aunty she is very naughty!" I joked to Kim. Really however I was so grateful... Money was just so tight for us then and even that extra tenner meant we could buy extra food. Spirit knew I wouldn't have dreamt of charging Kim and her friend for a reading as I knew they were both so financially hard up. And even though I know this money on this day came from Kim's aunt, I sort of felt it was a gift from spirit also, to reward me for my work in delivering their messages to loved ones.

The messages that came through for the both of them were magnificent! Kim's friend even seemed a little freaked out at all the accurate information that was coming through about her life right from a little girl, through to the present day. Lost children came through, messages of ease and reassurance and they even gave us a few giggles! Many of the spirits that come through have a wonderful sense of humour and many work hard on putting a smile of their loved ones face. Even if it's just for a moment. On this occasion spirit showed me the tops of the woman's thighs, of whom I was giving the reading (Kim's friend) I saw all big black bruising. My instant response was "OOO! What's this you're showing me? What does it mean?" Sometimes if I am shown darkened areas on someone's anatomy it indicates to me there are problems in this area, then they usually go on to tell me what the problem is. Well... I have to say I was instantly concerned as the marks were so dark... To which quite a few spirits started to laugh! They were in hysterics in fact! Then they told me, they are nothing to worry about and that the receiver was just so clumsy she always hit her thighs and bruises easily, but then never remembers how the bruises got there. They found this quite amusing, however we are also trying to give reassurance to the receiver at the same time.

This made me somewhat chuckle also. What often happens when the spirit is feeling intense emotion... Whether it be sadness, concern, nervousness... They impress it onto me, so I feel it as if it were my own emotion. The amount of times I've cried when giving readings, but it's not me! It's the spirit putting their heart and soul into the message being given, through me. Well in this case the emotion was happy laughter... lovely... I forwarded to the receiver what was being said and how they found this all very funny, to which she replied "OH MY GOSH! I get these bruises come and go at the top of my thighs all the time and when I was sat on the toilet the other day I noticed them there again! I actually thought to myself at that moment like... Oh my Gosh... Have I got leukaemia or something? I thought it might actually be something serious!" Now imagine this being said in a really

Soonita Rockett

Essex accent by a pretty blonde young lady... Knowing what they know you can see why they found this so amusing. "It's Okay, honey," I said reassuringly. "They want you to know that it's really nothing to worry about."

I must also point out that the day I gave this lady her reading, she was wearing thick trousers and a long shirt. I had not seen her for a good couple of months before that, so there really was no way I could have known of any bruises on her legs at this time. What's more important is that the receiver knew this. Spirit also talked about the guy she was with and how this relationship would blossom and they would become very close. At the time if I recall rightly she was still feeling a little insecure within the relationship for whatever reasons. Then she was told that by Christmas she would be pregnant. I tell people that I am not a fortune teller, I only give what is given to me. If spirit choose to forward snippets of the future then I hand it over. They gave beautiful reassuring messages about the baby. A baby girl in fact. I saw this lady a few weeks ago at Tesco. She is heavily pregnant, expecting a girl! "Everything is as you said it would, Soonita!" She said to me. Bless her.

Some of my earlier messages given to people I still remember bits of. I suppose because it was all such an amazing thing for me! And as evidence that I was on the right lines at time. Now though I will be giving messages and forget everything that was said ten minutes earlier. In fact my memory on a whole is worse than ever! I think this is partly the work of spirit. Those messages are not for me, they are to be delivered to the hearts of those that come to receive them.

181

I have given so many now, two years on, that there is no way I can remember them all. The terrible thing is... what I always feel so rude for! Is that I will meet people a few months after giving them readings and not even remember their faces! I'm terrible with names, but usually remember faces... usually.

I have learnt to trust and I trust that even if I forward something to the receiver and they don't understand it, or feel they can't connect with it, that the spirit knows best... they have that deeper understanding to us. They see things we can't and from different angles. What happens a lot, is that once the receiver has left the reading... Maybe later that night, the following week, month or year even! They suddenly understand, or remember. Sometimes it might be something that hasn't happened yet, so at that moment the receiver can't accept or understand it... But I always tell them to just remember it, as it might piece together later on.

I used to feel awkward when that happened, like people were questioning my ability and just thinking I was wrong. The minute I got nervous and my own conscious thinking and mind kicked in, the more I would get wrong because my own logic came into play. You see... all my work with spirit comes from my own subconscious. It comes from a separate system in my brain where my own thoughts and mind form, which is why I can converse with the spirits in my head and hear their replies in my head... A lot goes on in my head! Let *me* tell you! Ha-ha!

It didn't take me long to build my confidence up with the readings I gave people. I learnt to just give what I got and not to question it. It would all somehow make sense to the receiver and that is all what mattered. It didn't have to make sense to me... they weren't my messages. It took me less than a year to learn of my ability and to use it effectively to give good readings. That's not me bragging.... Like I'm ultra-gifted and better than the rest! Certainly I am not... But once I realised the ability and gift that had been bestowed upon me, I wanted to learn as much as I could and as fast as I could, so that I could use it! I wanted to help people. I was so humbled and felt so blessed that I had been chosen by spirit to deliver their work, I wanted to be the best I could possibly be at it. They chose me for a reason and I wasn't about to let them down. I do truly think spirit recognised my efforts and bit by bit, day by day my ability strengthened and grew. There were certain times of my life that year that were harder to deal with and incredibly stressful and I think spirit held back on how much I received at first, so as to not interfere with the goings on in my personal life at the time.

By ten months into it I was confident... I believed, trusted and didn't question anymore... I was a good medium I have to say that for me to praise myself on anything is rare as I tend to judge myself very harshly, so I recognise myself that this an achievement. However... I also strongly believe that spirit will only give you what they feel you are ready to receive. All the times before they knew I wasn't quite ready, due to other life goings on, but they felt I was ready. This part of the unconscious mind is also like a muscle. Like any muscle, the more you use it the stronger it gets. The more people I connected with and gave readings to, the stronger I was getting at receiving the messages and seeing spirit. The more I meditated and the more healing I sent out to people the better I got... To the point where someone would just have to give me a name and ask that I send some healing to them and I would know exactly what was wrong with the person I was sending thoughts of healing to, knowing whether or not they were going to be all right, such as my mother's friend who I shall tell you in the next chapter.

A couple of days after Kim and her friend coming over another little moment occurred where I felt I was being rewarded by spirit. I was dropping off my little girl at school when one of the other mums came up to me asking if I minded giving another mum's husband a call. He had asked her to pass on his number to me as I had set up a little mobile beauty therapist business on the side, he wanted to arrange a surprise pamper session for his wife's birthday. I took his number and said I'd call him later that day. As soon as the children had gone into school I saw my friend who I usually gave a lift into work if I was going that way. That day, I was going that way. I asked if she wanted a lift. She was smiling away and said yes. I had an overwhelming urge to ask if she was all right as we walked to my car. Despite her smiles and chirpiness something told me something was making her sad. I blurted it out and even though at first she said she was fine and persisted as I just couldn't accept she was telling the truth. "Are you sure? You're not worried about anything? How's work?" With that she explained that actually she was quite worried about work and that she was looking for other work.

Boom! That was it! It all came flooding in then... I didn't even realise what I was doing at first. Without even realising it I was forwarding messages from spirit. As soon as she told me about looking for other work my instant response was "You are doing the right thing and you will be so much happier in your job. You will be more of your own boss and in a very managerial position, but it won't be in the same field of work as you're in now."

"I was thinking about coming out of sales actually." She said.

"Hmmm... You've had your confidence knocked at work recently haven't you?"

"Yeah I think I have... All this stuff going on with my boss and I think it has knocked my confidence."

"Your next position will be in the finance department and it will be a much more rewarding job, personally and financially."

"Well that's what I'm trained in and what all my qualifications are. I was thinking of looking at jobs in finance." I did not know she had qualifications in finance. Even though I gave her the occasional lift it was always small talk really. Suddenly I was getting to know a whole lot about her and she didn't even have to speak!

"You're worried about your girls though as well aren't you?" I went on and went into a few more personal details to which she confirmed everything.

Finally! The nail was hit on the head! I realised what I was doing and what was going on... "I'm so sorry!" I said, realising. "Are you thinking I'm a bit weird that I know all this? I'll explain to you in the car properly, but I'm just picking all this stuff off you. I didn't even realise I was doing it at first."

"Yeah I was thinking it's a bit weird," she replied. "You do seem to know a lot." We got in the car and I explained everything to her in brief. That I was a medium and how it works a little bit. I began driving and carried on talking. I told her that I would be more than happy to meet up sometime and do her a proper reading. I said that I thought it might help her and give her a little upliftment and guidance and that spirit had influenced that whole situation which just occurred so they were obviously trying to get through to let me know. She said how she would really like that and would be grateful if we arranged something soon... Well... That was it... She accepted it, and they all came flying in! They wanted to speak to her there and then! I was driving I remind you! I had never before given messages from spirit whilst driving... But then thank goodness I'm good at multitasking... Can you imagine if the traffic police got wind of that... There'd be a new law to add to the list...

No talking or texting on the phone whilst driving
And
No conversing with spirit while driving!

Thankfully we arrived at our destination safely... I'd given her a lot in this short time. I just started blurting everything. Her face bless her, when I finally stopped the car and looked at her. She was just so shocked over everything I had said and how accurate I was. Yet again I hit home on something raw and a bit close to the bone and the tears started flowing. The spirit that had come through wanted her to realise how special and important a person she really was, as they were recognising she wasn't feeling that way at the moment. Bless her... I really felt for her and could feel her sadness and anxiety at that moment. I said to her that I thought it would be better that we did the reading sooner rather than later as I felt she could really do with it.

In a funny sort of way the readings I give really are like a form of therapy and counselling. I've experienced it so many times in the readings I've given where the receiver has been feeling a certain way, but never had the words to describe it or even talk about it to people. Within a moment spirit convey messages that put all this mixed up emotion that person has been feeling and why they are feeling it, in the space of five minutes. "Bloody hell!" One person said..." months all this has been going through my head, trying to work it out and in two minutes they've just put my whole life into context and it's all just fallen into place!" They also give some fantastic advice on how to move forwards from this dilemma or situation, moment in their life and give words of love and reassurance at the same time. Of all the therapies I've studied I don't know of a better one than this!

I asked my friend if she was free that Saturday (which was two days later) and she said she was. We arranged to meet in our local Costa for coffee, where I would give her reading. Not the best place to do this work, but we didn't really have another choice, so it would have to do. If spirit had an issue with it I knew they just wouldn't allow the messages through, but they were obviously fine with it. That day the messages came through strong and clear. As soon as I got home from dropping off my friend I rang the ladies husband who wanted to arrange the pamper session for his wife. I assumed he would be booking in advance for the next couple of weeks, but he wanted me to come over to give his wife the treatments, the same Saturday I'd arranged to meet my friend at Costa! He asked for me to come round in the morning and I'd arranged to meet my friend early afternoon. It all fitted in perfectly! Plus, I was going to be getting £50 for the treatments I was to give that day. As I thought about it again... I know I was getting paid for the beauty treatments, but I felt this was also payment for the reading I was to give. Two hours with my client and two hours with my friend... £50 wasn't bad for four hours work and I wouldn't have dreamt of charging my friend for the reading I had offered her. I offered that as a friend and because I wanted to help her.

Saturday came and I still felt strongly my theory to be true... Spirit were rewarding me for my work. During the reading beautiful messages came through for my friend and a lot of guidance of how to cope with certain situations and what was to come. Sometimes spirit may give us little glimpses of the future. Either as a little warning, or to give hope and something for the receiver to look forward to. I don't know how, but somehow, they know... A relative of my friends who had recently passed came through with lots to say. I said that I was being shown a beautiful photo and the lady looked gorgeous with all the gold jewellery on her face and a red and gold sari coming over her head. I said it was a wedding photo and clearly a Hindu wedding ceremony. There was so much love in the faces of the bride and groom as they looked into each other's eyes. "Oh Wow!" my friend said in disbelief. You're describing the photo that his wife put in his coffin before he was cremated. She wanted him to take it with him. It was their wedding photo."

Later that evening I decided to give myself a little Angel card reading. Sometimes when I'm feeling a little lost or need some guidance and reassurance, the cards can help me. It's another way of me hearing spirit and their guidance. As I was putting them away my hubby came to sit next to me. "Oh... You putting them away?" That's his way of saying "Can you give me a reading?"... And he has a go at me for not being more direct and to the point! I did his card reading then a spirit reading where his grandfather came through to give more personal guidance and to elaborate on what the cards were saying.

After the reading Chris decided to get cheeky with the spirits! "So!" he began, "If those cards were really meant for me and chosen by the angels..." Yeah, he'd had a bit of beer by this point... "Surely... If I shuffle these cards again and pick another four... the same four cards as before should come out." I said that in theory I suppose that should be the case and I know for me it's happened a few times. "Let's see shall we?" He tested... He put the cards he chose for the reading back into the deck and in all different parts of the pack. He sat for ages shuffling them, in which time I forwarded to him what I had just been told. "You're going to pick two the same and two different." I said.

He chose his four cards and put them face down in my hand. I turned the first one over and sure enough it was the same... But was that just a fluke? I turned over the second card and it was another, the same as before. We both burst out laughing at the coincidence, then in anticipation I turned the last two over together. They were different from before, just as spirit had said. I was just as surprised as Chris! I don't know why... I was told by trusting spirit, but I think as we were getting so carried away and having a bit of a laugh with it all I questioned myself for a moment and if I'd heard right (plus I'd had a little tipple myself, hehee).

Well... After that he was off on one! "Ask 'em how long I've got to stay in my crappy job for!" As I always tell people... I don't have to ask them for you... They can hear you too. Before he even finished his sentence I was told the answer. "Four years," I told him instantly. To this news he sighed with frustration as he did not enjoy the job he was in that much. At his response the spirit went on... "Don't look a gift horse in the mouth." Straight away he realised his reaction and that he was actually very lucky to be in a stable job that was putting food in our mouths, especially considering the times we live in and the recession. He soon perked up again though asking "Am I ever gonna win the lottery?" I laughed at spirits response... They are so clever! "Ha ha ha! They said that if you buy a scratch card tomorrow you're guaranteed to win at least a tenner!"

"Right!" he said, taking another sip of his beer... "I'm buying me a scratch card tomorrow!"

You never guess what... We only did win a tenner on a card the next day! I tell you it bought the biggest smile to my face. I'd had a rubbish evening and was feeling a bit down. Chris had gone to bed and hadn't scratched the card we'd bought. I saw it there and without even thinking about what had been said the night before I scratched it. Only when I saw the £10 win did I remember what had been said and I smiled. "Thank you, spirits" I said out loud in the kitchen. I had bought one more and went to scratch it thinking there's no way this will be a winner as well... I only won £20 more on the next one! I was proper chuffed! Ha ha!

Christian had left me £40 to pay for my daughter's street dancing lessons the next day and our KFC treat after. I would still have been a fiver short, plus I needed another £10 to buy more food for the dogs. If I hadn't of won that money on the lottery I was going to have to borrow some cash off my dad for a couple of days till Chris's next pay day. "Great!" I thought... We're sorted. I put the winning cards on the pin board in the kitchen for me to cash in the next day. Chris only saw them in the morning before going to work, so decided to take £20 out of my purse to put petrol in his car a few days earlier to get it out the way. I didn't know this when I went into the shop to cash in my winning cards, so bought a few groceries with what I thought I had extra. There was also two other cards I had to cash in with a total of three pounds on, so I exchanged three pounds for three more cards. When I got home I saw a message on my phone from my darling Chris, letting me know he'd taken the money. Well... I was back to square one. After buying the dog food I was still a fiver short to cover street dancing later on. Thanks babe! Bless him, he didn't realise.

Later that evening I told my daughter to get ready early as we had to pop to granddads before setting off to go street dancing. Good ol' dad! Always to our rescue. Just as we were about to leave I had a last minute thought. Just in case I'll scratch those other cards. Not that I thought I'd win anything, but just on the off chance... I won five pounds! Not two pounds, or ten... Five pounds! The exact amount I was short of. Really? Still a coincidence? I don't think so! And guess what else... My good friend Tommy had been round earlier that day and I'd given him a reading free of charge. Spirit had rewarded me yet again! The spirits truly are at work and I was more than grateful!

Chapter 19

My Mothers Best Friend

On one particular occasion that stands out in my mind is when I received a text message from my mother. It just read...

Don't mean to bother you but can you send some healing to Karen my friend from work, you met in London. She is very ill in intensive care Scunthorpe hospital. She needs all the help she can get. Lots of love take care Mum xx
(sent 16:04 5thOct 2012)

As you can see from the message, she didn't give anything away as to the reason why her friend was in hospital. Just that she was in a bad way. I remember I'd had a really busy day that day and was rushing around sorting dinner after getting my little girl home from school. I read Mum's message and was very concerned for her, but didn't have time at that moment to just stop and meditate to send healing. However... Weirdly half an hour later I managed to find the time...

Amongst all the chaos around me and trying to work to a schedule of getting my little girl fed, washed and into bed on time... Time just seemed to stand still and almost in a trance I took myself to the bedroom, alone, and went into meditation. Spirit knew I was needed and I was beckoned...

I opened myself to the world of spirit and asked my Mary to guide me to the hospital in Scunthorpe where I was to give healing to my mother's friend. I knew Mary would know exactly who she was and where to take me as I had met Karen twice before. Who I meet, my Mary meets, for she is always with me. White lights flashed before as I felt myself being taken to the hospital. I even felt motion in my stomach as if on a fast journey to some place. Before I knew it I was stood in the room with Karen at the hospital. Right before me I watched her rifling in pain, yet somewhat out of it she seamed and unconscious. My Mary was stood next me, holding my hand for reassurance. I can only describe it as like a scene from the movie "Scrooge". We were invisible to all the doctors and nurses working around her, yet I saw them clear as anything.

Mary looked over to me and said that Karen had just been given a high dose of morphine that should start to work soon. I looked at Mary with concerning eyes and asked if Karen was going to be OK. I wanted to hear her say yes, so I could give the reassuring news to my mum and make her feel better, give her hope. But Mary just looked at me with loving, deep understanding eyes and a slight motion of her head which said it all. She wasn't going to make it. However she told me that Karen wasn't going to go without a good fight as she didn't feel ready to go. She told me the least I could do was to help her right now and soothe her pain, to put her at peace.

I watched the doctor and nurses leave her room, then I stepped forward at Karen's bedside. As I looked her up and down it was if I was seeing her from the inside. I could see the insides of her body, where the problems were and what the problems were. This gave me an idea what areas to focus more so on when giving the healing, to ease as much pain as possible. What I saw was a darkened area down one side of her body and saw something leaking into her stomach and spreading through veins slowly around the rest of her body. I knew instantly it was her liver area and that there was something going into her stomach. I saw a thick tar like substance, all gloopy, trying to work its way through and I knew there was an infection. I also knew straight away that it was the infection getting into her blood that was slowly killing her. I firstly started working on trying to release some of the toxins from her body, but as I saw her in such pain before me I realised that this was something to be done later. Right now she needed pain relief. As I sent my soothing healing energies into her I watched her slowly begin to calm, until finally she seemed out of pain and at ease. She was now in a deep sleep.

It was at this point I asked for something I had never asked of before in my healing work... I asked for help from other spirits. Spirits in loving connection with Karen who wanted to help. I moved my own position to stand above Karen's head at the top of the bed. As I looked up two spirit men had joined me and a beautiful lady with long golden wavy hair in her forties. Just from the way the women acted I knew straight away this was Karen's mother (I did not know at this time that Karen's mother had passed away). The lady sat on Karen's hospital bed and took her hand. She bought the hand to her lips and kissed it, then held it to her cheek caressing it. She looked sad for what her daughter was going through. She put down her hand then stroked her hair looking loving into her daughters face. I just watched this beautiful, intensely emotional and amazing scene take place before... I felt so humbled to see this moment. A mother come back for her daughter... She then stood and held out both her hands. I instinctively knew my instruction and we all joined hands around the hospital bed to give group healing to Karen. Towards the end I was told that I was to come back at 2am as she would need us again for healing. I was also told to pass on messages to my mother (as if they came directly from Karen) that she wanted my mother to spend as much as time as possible at the hospital with her, even if it meant lying to the nurses about being family. She said that my mother was like a sister to her and that she was tell the hospital she was her sister, so she would be allowed to visit. She also mentioned a holiday that was talked about between them and that whatever happens my mum must go still, and that she will be there with her every step of the way. I was told by other sources at that moment that when Karen passes my mother must not go straight to a medium seeking her. I was told that it was going to take time for Karen to be able to come through as she needed healing time and time to come to terms with her fate and new life.

I hesitated after this to call my mother. What do I tell her? I knew she wanted reassurance from me, but I didn't want to give her false hopes. I also did not want to be the bearer of bad news. I decided I would just tell her I really didn't know whether she would be OK or not, but just to keep hoping and praying for her. That's not quite how the conversation ended up though... My mum... *She wouldn't stop*... She wanted answers! And she knew I knew more than I was letting on. I started by explaining to her what I had seen. She confirmed that she had started off with problems in her liver which had spread to her pancreas, causing infection in her stomach. I pre warned mum that the intense pain, deliriousness and sweating I saw was caused as the infection had got into her blood and was poisoning her body. My mother, being a nurse, confirmed that these were indeed symptoms of blood poisoning. Remember I did not know any of this before going into meditation.

After giving all this evidence, including seeing Karen been given the morphine, mum wanted more answers. She had received a call just before I rang to say that Karen had been given a dose of morphine and was now resting. She had been induced into a coma so as to not feel the immense pain she was suffering. Mum was shocked at how much I had picked up through the healing session. She truly believed I was in the room with her friend, which meant a lot to me... I can completely understand people thinking I'm a bit doo-lally chatting this kind of chatter, but I suppose the evidence I give is what glows its truths.

I told my mum of the three spirits that joined me around the bed. I gave the names of the spirits and mum confirmed the lady to be Karen's mother who passed away in her forties and one man to be a brother. The other man I assume was an uncle, but my mother couldn't place him. She was very to the point... "Is she going to live?" she kept asking... "You know don't you? I can tell from your voice you know..." Finally I gave in. I told my mum everything I had been told, but I reassured her that I was going to keep sending healing and prayers and who knows what miracles may occur... I didn't want her to lose hope.

I waited up that night to send more healing at the time I had been summonsed for... 2am. This time again I could see Karen rifling in agony. Grunting, squirming and wriggling before me. I went to work straight away, putting all my energies into her and driving away the pain. Within a couple of minutes she simmered down until once again she looked at peace. I sat with her a few moments. As I looked up I saw her mother there in the room... Just waiting. As I woke early in the morning with my daughter (the child does not know the meaning of a LIE IN!) I was eager to find a moment again to send more healing for Karen. Despite what I had been told I myself did not want to give up hope for Karen's recovery. I knew how much she meant to my mother and what a good beautiful person she was... I wanted her to live. For my mother's sake.... However this time when I went to give the healing, there was a block... I was told that I have done all I can and that I have at least helped her by easing her suffering. I was told that I must now leave her to progress on her journey and my healing was no longer required, only my prayers to help her on.

I rang my mother that evening. As I told her everything my mother confirmed that Karen sure enough did awaken in agony at ten to two in the morning and was given more morphine. "You were right," she said "She did need you at that time". She also confirmed that between the hours of 5am and 8am she suffered three heart attacks. It was about 8am that I sat to send healing that morning and there was a block... Maybe spirit thought this would be just too upsetting for me to see... I don't know... The hospital had told my mother that if Karen was to have another heart attack in the next forty eight hours, they would not resuscitate her again. We all prayed for her. There even came signs of hope over the following week or so as she showed signs of improvement. She remained unconscious the whole time. Nearly two weeks later she finally passed away. She sure did put up a fight.

Chapter 20

The Angels Beckon

The first time I was visited by an angel, I sat in meditation in the development group I had gotten into. It was run by a ninety-six year old lady who had been a practicing medium for over sixty years and known worldwide... Didn't she like to remind people of that! At heart she was a beautiful caring soul, however on the surface she carried a lot of ego and could be very judgemental and harsh in her ways. She could be very belittling, yet make out it was absolutely necessary for your learning. I still question that now, though I guess I learnt quickly how NOT to be. If ever a valuable lesson was learned. Knowing this lady is who made me realise, that working with spirit and as a medium, does not make you saintly and all knowing... Working with spirit is merely the tip of the iceberg... Mastering the self, is the biggest accomplishment one can truly achieve in any one life time.

When reporting back on our meditations, she would often end my report on a note of me being very creative with my imagination and that everything received was somehow wrong... I learnt to be very strong and trust my heart here, though would still at times question myself due to the added dose of ego from that lady. Then one day I met the Archangel Gabriel in my meditation at circle. I knew our leaders thoughts on angels already, so was very careful to how I gave this report... The beautiful Archangel Gabriel came to me. She placed her hand upon my heart and told me she brings a message from God. She told me I carry Gods love in my heart and am to let the light of this light shine bright for all to see. I am a teacher and a messenger and God calls me to deliver to the people. The love this beautiful angel surrounded me in made it hard to fight back the tears of emotion that waved over me.

I didn't share the full contents of this meditation to our leader, but did stay strong to say it felt like an angel and was so beautiful... "Ah let me stop you there!" she interrupted abruptly... "There are no angels! All these years I have done this work and have never come into contact with angels... They are made up! What you probably saw was a guide, which is why the energy was stronger. There cannot be angels, Where is the logic in that?" Well... I remember thinking... We talk to dead people! Where is the logic in that? You see there is no logic to any of this... Logic is man-made, the human brains way of interpreting and sorting something out... With this work, you follow your heart, you listen to your dreams and interpret what feels right. Logic knocks every last bit of my work out the water. Faith, trust and knowing keeps it in my heart.

It was at this point I knew for sure I had to leave this group. I had not been a part of it for long, and to be honest did not learn an awful lot. My main teachings came from direct... Spirit... And now were starting to extend further into other realms. I began receiving teachings from Ascended Masters and my guardian angels began introducing themselves to me also. My world was spiralling from all I had ever known in this life... But I loved it. What an adventure!

Different Archangels would visit me in meditation. I have never known much about different angels, except Angel Gabriel in the nativity plays... So they would introduce themselves to me in a way, that when I went to find anything more out about this particular angel, I would gain instant confirmation. As this was still all very new to me, sadly their word was not always enough. I would still doubt myself to what I was receiving, to being true or just my imagination. This I now know to be my ego being unsettled with my new learnings. Trying to hold me back out of fear and simply not understanding the new world I was delving into.

As I meditated on my bed, almost instantly the image of what I could only describe as looking like a gladiator. He was so tall and powerful in his presence. His muscles defined, his hair golden and eyes as blue as the purest ocean. He bought my attention to his feet, to which he wore gladiator type sandals, laces weaving up his muscular leg. He said only "I am the Archangel of Strength. You have nothing to fear, I am here to protect you always. I love you."

The same evening I felt the urge to look on Amazon if there were any books on angels I could find, that might help me learn or understand angels more so... Since more and more were starting to visit me. One book jumped out at me and I just knew I had to get this one. It was a book on Arch Angel Michael by Doreen Virtue. I ordered it hesitantly, as money was tight, but I knew I had to get it. Little did I know that this guidance was coming from more than intuition. The book arrived a week later and as I read more of its contents it was confirmed to me absolutely, that the angel that came to me that day, was indeed Arch Angel Michael. The book was a compilation of other people's experiences with this beautiful angel of Strength. One lady described her tell-tale sign of knowing Arch Angel Michael is with her, by the gladiator styled sandals worn upon his feet.

Some of the most beautiful meditations I had were those with my guardian angels. They showed themselves to me at first in long robes with big hoods over their heads and faces. There were six of them. I still have not got to know each of them individually, but what a beautiful feeling just to know they are with me every step of my journey. Through various meditations another one of my guardians may show themselves to me. They have taught me so much about guardian angels and their roles to me and others.

When I see guardian angels with others, it is a sight and a blessing to behold. I might see someone with just the one and others with three or four. I have been told that the more guardian angels that one person holds with them, is how many needed for this lifetime on the Earth. So if I see someone with four guardian angels in their energy fields, I know instantly that person has had much trials and tribulations to overcome in their journey, or will soon to have... I always ask their angels what I see and why, before speaking to the person.

In one reading I forwarded for a lady, the message from her guardian angels was "The most powerful love known to man on the Earth is that between mother and child." To this lady that was absolutely true. She could understand this love, being the doting mother of two. This is the most powerful love in her life that she will ever know. To give her some understanding to how much her guardian angels loved her they said, "Take that love and times it by ten... And that is still not close to how much we love you." All I know from the connection with my own angels and other people's, is that this is a love completely above and beyond human comprehension. It is a love so pure and so beautiful. Our guardian angels choose to be with us in this lifetime. Promising to never leave our sides through every step of this earthly journey. They are beings that have spent many life times over with us, in this world and others. They know our souls inside out and love us deeply.

As I sat in meditation with my guardian angels, another stepped forward to reveal themselves to me. I wasn't overly surprised to see that this guardian was not a being of this planet. As many thought to be fictional images of aliens, true to form my guardian angel was not of this planet. With his elongated oval head, with big black piercing, beautiful deep eyes, his long skinny neck and body and long fingers... As alien as you can imagine, yet emitting such an intense radiation of love. I knew straight away I had spent a lifetime with this being on another planet. That star planet in fact to be Sirius. Since then I have learnt much about our Earthly links with the planet Sirius, dating back into ancient civilisations. But this is a tale for the following book to this.

I began getting flashbacks to one year previous to me seeing this beautiful guardian of mine in meditation. On our honeymoon me, hubby and our five year old, were all sleeping in the same bed in our beautiful villa in Madeira... As you do on honeymoon. Anisha didn't like sleeping alone in different places. She slept between us and facing me. As we slept face to face, at the same moment we both opened our eyes... There was no noise to wake us, it was an intuitive moment we both shared. At the same time we slowly turned our heads to look into the open door of the bathroom of our en suite. We had the night lamps on in the bedroom and bathroom door open to allow extra light into the room, as none of us were too keen on the dark.

As we looked into the bathroom we both saw a perfect alien looking figure stood in the door way. It was one of those moments where it takes a minute to comprehend. Anisha turned and pushed her face into my chest saying "Mummy, who's that man in the bathroom?" Strangely, though alien in form, we both sensed a male energy with this figure. I comforted her telling her everything is OK and began trying to wake Christian, beside us. I was waking him to the words of "Baby, wake up! There's a man in our bathroom!" I spoke this in a loud whisper whilst nudging the life out of him! As he stirred all the electrics blew. The lights went out in the whole villa and it was pitch black.

Chris got up to check the bathroom straight away and there was no one. All the windows in there were locked and there would have been no way for anyone to have got in or out. Christian and my brother began checking everything out. It seemed to just be our villa, as all the street lights were still on. They checked the fuses and there was no apparent reason for this to have happened. We decided the only thing we could do, was to go back to bed and ring the agency in the morning to sort it out. The second our heads hit the pillow, all the lights came back on! There wasn't anything to explain this and it didn't happen again whilst we were there. Anisha and I strangely never spoke of what we both saw that night. Though the next day it crossed my mind, I didn't want to remind her, as thought it might be best for her to forget anyway. She never, ever mentioned it, until just over a year later... The very next day of me having my meditation with my Sirius light being Angel.

As we walked over to the park after school she turned to me and said, out of the blue... "Mummy? Do you remember when we were in Madeira and all the lights went out? There was that funny looking man in our bathroom wasn't there?" I am always very honest with my daughter, especially where any of these understandings lay, as I try my hardest to deter from confusion at such a young age. "Yes, my darling." I replied. "I didn't think you remembered about that."

"I do, Mummy... Was he one of your angel friends?"

"Yes, darling." I replied with a smile on my face. "He was." What a thing for a six year old to say. And to even associate this being as one of my angels? My little girl has a knowing so deep. She is wise beyond our words and has her own beautiful, connection with the angels.

During meditation with my light being angel of Sirius, the first thing he said to me was "You have seen me in this life before." I remembered instantly, thinking how could I ever have allowed this moment to have slipped my mind. As I spent time with him in meditation, I felt my soul remembering a love so deep for this being and I felt his love for me. I felt honoured and so grateful that this being of my past life, would give of himself, to remain with me in this lifetime. Our guardian angels help us through life in many ways. Some would have carried traits in their own incarnations that feel you would benefit from in this lifetime. They work on impressing those traits into our character and personality to help us when needed. They give us strength when we feel down and weak, they inject us with determination when all around us seems worthless. They infuse us with courage, inspire us with ideas, uplift us when we are down and wipe away our tears during times of our lowest. They encase us in their wings to comfort us, lie down beside us when we feel alone and guide us continuously. All it takes is for us to stop... Listen... And feel. Each and every one of us on this earth, are blessed with our own guardian angels, that are for us... And for each of us, only...

I have received much healing from the Master. Unconditional, warm and tender love and understanding from the angels. I have been taken on many journeys to help me understand many world occurrences and my own emotional wellbeing. In one meditation, my sweet guide Mary took me to a lake. She told me to immerse completely into the water and just swim. I was told to enjoy the healing qualities of the water I was in, the water of purity in the heavens... and to take in the beautiful scenery as the sun shone big and bright on the horizon... I did so for some time. It was beautiful and breath-taking. I absolutely did feel uplifted and cleansed.

As I came to the edge of the lake to climb out, a hand reached for me. As I was helped up to land I recognised the soul immediately. It was Jesus. "Walk with me," he said, radiating love so strongly. As we walked around the edge of the lake, he lifted his arm to gesture a look in that direction. As I looked across a fantastically green field, I saw a mother smiling lovingly at her baby on her lap. She tickled him and the baby giggled, looking so lovingly back to his mother. The mother I saw was an angel, with wings blossoming up and around her in a glow of light. Then Jesus took back my attention and asked me to sit opposite him on a tree stump.

He then said to me... "You are our angel on the Earth, to give what we angels here cannot. There is only so much we can do." It was at this time I was very down about going to the development group I was in, yet feeling guilty to stop, like I may be giving up and letting spirit down. I also hated leaving my family on an evening, especially for something I wasn't enjoying, then sometimes making me feel rotten for the next couple of days... Purely due to cruel words often spoken by the leader... Jesus went on to say, "Anisha is fine with her father one evening a week and that this time for them alone together is a blessing and their time for bonding. The more you give of yourself, the more we give to you." I felt this was given in the spiritual sense and the strength of my abilities and knowledge and wisdoms shared. "Lose your fears, trust... and allow me to lead the way." With this, Jesus got up and began walking away, with a gesture for me to follow. I followed back into myself and my reality, knowing that my path was being guided by this wise sacred figure.

Two weeks after this meditation I met Nicola. I went along to the church that evening to help out and watch the medium of the night at work. The medium was Nicola Farmer. As I sat at the very back of the hall, Arch Angel Gabriel appeared at my side. With such love and tenderness she leaned over to me, resting her head on mine and placing her arm around me. Again feeling a little down and confused about things, she gave me an instant upliftment, then told me to listen to this lady who was our medium. She told me this lady was someone to trust. Within moments of this, Nicola came to me in the audience. Her messages were perfect and beautiful. My granny had come through for me. The message that came through was perfect understanding to me and confirming everything my granny had said to me in meditation, days before. I thought Nicola would be interested to know the meaning to this message as there was a lesson for all, within it.

My granny had told me that she had worked hard in the spirit realms, so that she could progress into the place she was now in, giving her the ability to be another true guide to me, in spirit. In a place she could help me ultimately. This was a teaching for me, that spirit family could do this to help us on our journeys. My teacher of that time was always very adamant that we cannot communicate with our own families in spirit. That it is not allowed... Yet again my own teachings from spirit were proving otherwise. I trusted more what was given from them, though would still get confused at times and allow my own ego to misguide me or doubt myself. I wouldn't normally hassle the medium after their demonstration as lots of others would and I didn't want to be another. However I felt a strong urge to share this with her. I waited at the back until others had spoken to her, then approached her. I was very apologetic at first to be taking any more of her time, then shared what I wanted with her.

She just stared at me, then asked to sit with me a moment. I was very grateful for her time and felt at instant ease with this lady. She told me that absolutely you can speak to family members is spirit and that it was sad I had been told otherwise. Before I told her anything, she told me that I was sitting in the wrong circle. I confirmed to her that I had been feeling that way and felt very confused about everything. She then went on to tell me I had a beautiful connection with the angels. I was almost in tears as I finally found someone I could open up to about this side of me. Someone I felt understood and didn't think I was crazy!

She startled me even more to say there is a being with you not of this planet. I told her this was one of my guardian angels. She then asked if I understood the name Mary. I told her this was my spirit guide. I went on to tell her how she helped me so much and made me feel so loved. Truly like a mother's love I had never known. I said laughing, that I often call her "Mother Mary" as she is so maternal and loving, just like a mother to me in spirit. With this, Nicola said to me with loving eyes, "Can I tell you something? Your guide IS Mother Mary." I began to cry. I told her that I had often thought this, yet told myself it couldn't be... And now this beautiful soul was confirming it for me. Nicola gave me her number. She herself run classes and invited me to join. My wise sacred guide had lead me to this Angel of the Earth. It was the start of new beginning's, understandings and phenomenal learning. I will always be grateful of this meeting.

Chapter 21

My Healing Journey

Through beautiful meditations with the angels and Ascended Masters, I had received wonderful healing and understandings. I was prompted to look back in time, at certain events in my life that may have caused upset. For the first time I was looking back at these moments through different eyes... Through the eyes of the angels. I was seeing the situations from every angle and each person's role played within these moments of my history. I was seeing with love, compassion and new understandings. These meditations helped me greatly, though they were not quite enough to release certain hurts completely. I had some very deep seated issues to release from my energetic fields. No matter how hard I would try to mask it, or even *think* that I was over it! Sometimes, we think we have released certain things from our past, but the dark energy of that pain still remains within our energy, occasionally showing itself through the way we react to life around us.

I went along to one of my classes with Nicola, where only three of us could make it that particular evening. As a result, Nicola felt to share with us some of the new work she was delivering, as part of her services to humanity. She gave an understanding of energy and entity clearings of our spiritual and physical being. This is a ceremony performed with the assistance of the Archangels and Masters, carried out in safety, with absolute protection.

The idea is to release entities of other spirit energies which may have become attached to our energy fields, showing itself through some of our own behaviours. Clearings can also release the body of dark residual energies, left as a marker of past trauma. The benefits from this are profound! Dark energy within the body can grow and grow, with the hardship of life itself. These darker forming energies can begin to manifest into the more physical form triggering illness and even cancers within the physical body. From a scientific stance, we would refer to the body's reactions to trauma and stress with the release of cortisol within the body. The body reacts to exterior stresses by releasing a chemical called cortisol. This chemical is more so known as the stressor hormone. An over secretion of this hormone into our circulatory system can cause high levels of stress and even depression, leading on to other mental illness.

High levels of cortisol in our blood can start to deteriorate the physical body causing fatigue, irritability, restlessness and illness, as it eats away at our immune system. As the immune system breaks down, we become more susceptible to viruses and other illnesses around us. For my final year dissertation at

Uni, I carried out research on reception aged children, to determine whether the age of four/five/six was a good age for UK children to start school, or six years old? In countries such as Switzerland, Australia and America, children start full time school at the age of six. This is with the understanding that once young children's social and emotional needs have been met and learned appropriately, only then are they ready for academic learning.

There are also studies supporting this practice, demonstrating certain brain development of children at the different ages. By six years old, all the biological wirings of the brain have been connected, which in turn gives the child the understanding necessary, for tasks such as reading, writing, problem solving and emotional empathy for others. At the age of six, when the child starts school, they begin with excelled learning of new subjects and tasks. Research taken across the world, shows how children who start school at this later age have gone on to perform and achieve higher than those starting school at a younger age. Many children who start later, also show much higher levels of confidence and self-esteem.

My personal research carried out, highlighted the impact on the child's physical wellbeing, as well as emotional and behavioural changes. It was very apparent the increased suffering of illness for many reception children in their first year at school. This can be argued that being within the new group environment, it was just their immune systems building a tolerance, however all of these children had previously attended nurseries, so were used to being in group environments. In actual fact, when placing yourself in the heart and mind of a four year old... Some children only just turning four a couple of weeks before starting school... Having to adapt to a new, usually large building, with lots of different staff to get used to, where they are not as supportive to their personal needs like the nursery staff... Having to conform to new understandings and expectations of themselves, with a firmer tone than previously used to... Actually can be incredibly stressful for a young child.

This stress clearly impacts them physically as looking across most schools of Britain, reception years demonstrate the highest rates of absences. I have used this research to show an example of increased stressor hormones within the body and its immediate effects it can take on. However this kind of stress can usually be overcome with time and eventually work its way out of the system. When I say system, I mean within the physical and energetic body, causing no long term damage. Sometimes with masses amounts of stress, the energetic body can become clogged up, then starts to stick to its carrier. This is the energy known as residual energy... And you can imagine the prolonged impact to any traumatic stresses from past experiences. There are many other studies you can read up on, which research everything mentioned here.

By reading through this scientific jargon, you can begin to understand how the biological, physical make-up of the body and the energetic fields of the body (which many refer to as the spirit body within) are so closely interlinked, they are literally as one. So if trauma causing physical outlets on the body can be released through medicine and surgery? Equally it can be diminished from the body using energy. When we begin to start seeing ourselves as the pure energy fields that we really are and break through the illusion of all its physical restraints, we begin to see the possibilities open to us... I knew that degree wasn't a waste of time. Now getting back to my energy clearing with Nicola!

Having told us a little about the ceremony, how it works and how it can help us, she gave each of us a treatment by performing the ceremony on us. It was incredible. As deep seated energy was being resurfaced, it gave you an over rush of emotion. We all cried, but that is part of it. Crying is another outlet, a release. Feeling the love of the angels around me at that time and knowing something quite remarkable had just taken place, I felt uplifted, lighter and happy.

The next day however, I was in a foul mood! I just could not shake it. Everything annoyed me! I couldn't understand it. Hearing how others felt as a result after this ceremony, I felt rather disappointed that I felt so aggressively low!

Though it all became clear the next day... So the next day after the ceremony I felt rubbish, then I went to sleep that night, to have one of the most strange, yet incredibly healing dreams I had ever experienced. I dreamt Christian and I arrived at this big house, then who should come to the door, but Zac. I haven't seen Zac for fourteen years! And as you can imagine, didn't leave him on the best of notes. He came to the door smiling and very thankful that we had come.

We sat on his sofa, both of us at first seeming rather uncomfortable with where we were and our company. Zac couldn't do enough for us, getting drinks and snacks to the table and trying hard to make small friendly chatter. I was having none of it... Then I was surprised to see my Christian warming to his charms. I started to feel a little hurt and betrayed by this too. How could he, knowing what this guy had put me through, to sit laughing and joking with him! I contained my emotions, but stayed quiet. It struck me as to how much Zac seemed to be trying so hard with Christian, but not paying too much attention to me... Besides the odd warming smile in my direction. I felt very uneasy, my mind racing. What was he playing at?

Later in the dream our evening came to an end and Christian and I got up to leave. Zac walked us to the door. We all stood just outside the front door, Zac and Christian shaking hands saying their goodbyes, when Christian realised he had forgot his scarf. "Oh! I think it's on the bed upstairs!" Zac said. Christian quickly ran back into the house shouting that he would get it, before anything else could be said. What was wrong with him? I thought, feeling more annoyed that now he was leaving me alone with Zac! Zac pulled the door to, so Christian wouldn't over hear, then turned me to face him, gently... "Great." I thought... "Here we go again."

Then surprisingly he began to speak softly, apologising for everything he put me through in the past. He said how he understands the pain I went through and can see the harm he had caused. He began to cry saying how sorry he was and that believe or not, he loved me and has never stopped. He went on to say how he liked Christian and was happy for me, as long as I was happy. My heart began to melt and the anger wash away. I suddenly didn't only see the Zac that stood before me... I saw deeper and deeper into his heart. A mass of understanding as to why a human being could come to being so cruel to another was interpreted into my heart, as I saw elements of his own past, which softened my heart further. I wiped the tears from his cheek, looked deep into his eyes and told him "I forgive you." He released a sigh of relief and gratitude, then rested his head on mine for a moment as he went to kiss my cheek. In the moment of that kiss, a flood of love washed over me and that is where I awoke.

I was confused to say the least! It played over and over in my mind, until I sat later that morning to meditate over it. I was confused, but felt somehow uplifted and lighter. How could I genuinely feel love for someone that had caused such harm and hurt to me in the past... I am not just speaking of in the dream. I woke up still feeling love for this man and so warm towards him. Things were starting to make sense slowly and I couldn't get the dream, or him out of my thoughts. I kept this as no secret from my husband, who weirdly was being very calm and understanding about it. Through meditation and guidance from the great Arch Angel Raphael all became clear.

Christian was and always has been my protector, therefore in the dream Zac knew he had to gain Christians trust in order to get to me. This is why at first he didn't even attempt conversation with me. Once he had achieved this, he gained his opportunity to get me alone, which was needed so that he could speak from his heart, and I could accept without worrying about Christian and what he would think. The forgiveness had taken place from the heart and a space of pure love, which was necessary for me to ultimately release everything that this time in my life had imprinted on me.

Truly I had released it and felt wonderful for it. I no longer carried anger or hate for this man, strangely I understood him and felt only love and compassion... And for my Christian... I loved him even more, realising just what a huge role he plays in my life, as my love, my best friend and my guardian... My soul protector.

I asked Arch Angel Raphael what this means now? Should I make an effort to speak with Zac again? Arch Angel Raphael told me that what had happened had done so on a soul level and was necessary for me and my progression at this time. It was not necessary to ever have this man in my life again, for his Earthly self might still have some catching up to do with his higher, Godley self. I understood and I felt fine with this. I was proud of myself for this release and over the moon happy! It put me in a higher, happier place for weeks! I understood then, that the ceremony of energetic clearing had helped to surface some of the deeply seated and embedded pain that was in my very core. The anger and aggression I felt the next day was even further dragging it and unveiling it from its hidden depth, until all could be released within the realms of my dream world. I had let it go... And I was quick to get on the phone to Nicola and tell her all about it!

*

From the first class I attended of Nicola's, there were excited talks of a new powerful workshop she was about to begin. In order for Nicola to run this workshop in this country, she had to gain specialised teaching in Arizona to do so and give her the licence to teach it. How funny I should meet one of the only ladies in the country to teach this workshop, Awakening the Illuminated Heart (ATIH) By Drumvalo Melchizedek...? Or that she should live so close to me? She spoke briefly of the workshop, not going into too much detail of what it entailed or how it can help, but a voice from the angels sang clear in my ear, "You need to do this!" So my next question clearly was... "How much does it cost?" When she gave me the figures I put that workshop completely to one side in my thoughts, as there was no way I could afford that kind of money, that time in my life, or justify it when I was struggling to put food on the table! However, over the next few weeks, there was a niggling voice from within me that kept it playing in my thoughts.

As I laid one starry night on my daughter's trampoline, talking to Arch Angel Michael, I asked him why this workshop keeps playing on my mind and if I am to do it. His reply was that this workshop would indeed help me. Not so much in my work as a medium, but for my own wellbeing, necessary healing and the self. I replied jokingly to Arch Angel Michael that he thought then I need further fixing and healing? ... His answer was a short, sharp, yet loving "Yes!" I had no idea how I was going to get the money together.

The next morning I awoke like any other day, thinking what needs to be done on this particular one. As I remembered class with Nicola later that day, Mother Mary said to me, "Tonight when you go for class you will take Nicola £150 to secure as your deposit for the ATIH Workshop and you will book onto the February Workshop." My first reaction was that I didn't think we had that money to give, though my sweet Mary reassured me that my husband had it and that I am to ask him for the money. I thought about what she said, working things out in my mind. It was now November and getting past Christmas was always a bit of a struggle financially. January is normally playing catch up, but February should be fine to pay the rest. I was after all now getting a monthly wage working at my daughter's school.

Chris got home from work and I asked him for the money. He firstly told me he didn't have it. I told him I knew he had and that he needed to give it to me. To that, he said the only money he had in his account was that, that he had to pay the rent with the following week. He told me he couldn't touch it, as there was no way of replacing it before then. With that, I told him he just had to trust me and trust that the angels are truly guiding this to happen. "They wouldn't say it if everything wasn't going to be OK." He put his trust in me and the angels and gave me the money. Nicola kindly accepted the money as the deposit (as she would normally take more) and signed me onto the February workshop. Details of Nicola Farmer's website and workshops can be found in the back of this book.

The following week came, two days before the rent was due and still no sign of this money being replaced. I tried not to think about it, feeling rubbish that I may have to ask for help from my parents last minute, then I had an impulse to go and see my daddy. Not for money, just to spend time and maybe have some lunch with him. As I arrived he was cooking. It had been my birthday the week before. "Your aunty came at the weekend and left you a birthday card over there darling," my daddy said... I went to the card, opened it and out fell £150 cash. Just as the angels had said... Everything was OK. My aunty and father had no idea about the workshop, or money I had parted with previously.

Drawing close to the date I was due to do the workshop a very similar story unfolded, where yet again... The miracles of the angels work were clear to see. Especially considering how I stopped working the month previous to the workshop... However, these are stories I like to save for my live audiences. I attended the workshop amongst other beautiful people with shining hearts. I gained so much deeper knowledge and understanding from this workshop, along with the further guidance from the angels that assisted me through it. The world, the people, the universe began to make sense... More than ever I began to understand everything as one. The biggest journey of that workshop was the one of myself.

During the course of the workshop the clearing was performed again, though this time on a deeper level. As I laid on the bed to take my turn I thought to myself "Well, I can't see what else I have to release? I'm sure there's nothing else." Boy! Was I wrong! Part of the process for this was to feel yourself in the mother's womb. A place of love, to feel that protection and security. A place of pureness. As I delved back into that space I quickly realised that I felt very uncomfortable, to the point of panic! I instantly panicked to feel that I am meant to be in a beautiful place right now... But in my mother's womb was the last place I felt love. This made me question why? I unearthed many moments of insecurities from my past, realising them to all be stemming to this.

For whatever reasons, I had never felt accepted in my mother's eyes. I realised that throughout life it had meant too much to me, to feel accepted by others. Trying to replace the lack of acceptance from my mother. This would often lead to people pleasing behaviours, through actions that were not necessarily true to myself. Whenever I felt like people did not like or accept me, I would allow this to get to me, offend me and hurt me. Just to understand this part of me was powerful. It meant I could let go of past hurts unnecessary to my progression and understand why it might at times upset me, when others showed disapproval of me in any way. By understanding this, I can be quick to spot it and let it go, so that it no longer affects me. For now I felt happy just to understand, but I had not completely released.

The strangest thing was... If that's the word to bring understanding to the workings of energy and everyone and thing being connected... I laid on the bed for my turn of clearing at 3:45pm. My phone was turned off. When I turned my phone back on at about 5pm a message appeared from my mum. It read "Love you lots. Mum." That message was sent at 4:03pm. This would have been the time I retreated back into the mother's womb. That message meant so much to me. I was already at a place in my life where I accepted my mum and our relationship from the past, knowing that she did love me in her own way. Maybe just at times, not to my idea of love and how a loving mother should be. My expectations and ideas of a mother's love was very different to the love and care I received from my mother, but that did not make her wrong... Hence the danger of idealism and expectation.

The final straw of this hurt, I guess was when my mother left the family home, when her and my daddy separated and divorced. Even though I knew and understood why she had to do what she did, I still felt hurt that she also chose to leave me. Though on a conscious level I thought my parent's divorce had never really upset me, it clearly had affected me more than I ever realised. The clearing yet again had resurfaced some very deep hurts within me. Helped me understand myself more. That night I felt very emotional and tearful. On one hand I felt good that I had learnt to understand myself more, but on the other I felt sad that this still very much was a hurt I carried with me. I prayed hard that our activities in the workshop the next day, would help me to completely release. This was another dark aspect of myself I was being made to face head on. It was painful and at times a little scary... But so worth it, for the person I am today.

The next morning began with further healing. I was immediately taken on a journey with my dear sweet Mother Mary... "Now let me show you the truth of it all," she told me. She took me back to the mother's womb... Only this time I was seeing what was going on from the outside. I saw my mum looking in the mirror at her bulging tummy, smiling and feeling the love she held for me, before I was even born. I saw her knitting clothes for me as she imagined her baby wearing them in her arms. I saw my birth and the relief on my mother's face that I was healthy and okay. I saw her hold me in her arms for the first time, looking into my eyes and bursting with pride and overwhelming emotions. I saw the happiness on her face as I played in the bath with her and took my first steps... I felt my mother's love...

Mother Mary went on to tell me that all I had felt and perceived in my world, was the illusion that I chose to see my reality... For now I was being shown the true reality... All those years I'd missed it... How very sad... All because I had expectation and distorted illusions of reality. Every time my poor mother made what I classed as another mistake, I would use it as evidence to support my thoughts that she didn't really care or love me. Like some scientist searching for the truth... Finally I had found it. Now I truly was ready to let go. From this point on, I loved and valued my mother so much more. Forever in my heart she will be for an eternity xxx

Chapter 22

Dreams Come True...

Christian and I sat together one night, in our small hole of a home with the angel cards. These cards were bought for me from my sweet friend Tommy, who knew of my affinity with the angels. I did not ever read the instruction book of how to use my card. The angels were my guides. I quickly began giving very affective and accurate readings to myself and others with the angel's guidance and beautiful, uplifting words. Having just finished giving myself a little reading with the cards, Christian asked for a reading too. Though only a couple of cards were pulled for him, the angelic messages were flowing through endlessly. They linked the both of us in the end, giving guidance to help us out of our situation we felt very powerless in and stuck.

The angels told us to each get a piece of paper and write down our dreams and desires. They said they knew the house was one of them, but they wanted details of exactly what we wanted from this house. They told us to imagine ourselves already in our home, happy and living the dream. Describe details of what we see and how it would best suite us. We both did so. Strangely, though there was no conversing to each other whilst doing this, we had both written the same things. I think we had spoke of it enough!

Our only dream was our nice home. We had made the mistake of trying not to dream big, in case that would be greedy, or asking for too much. Genuinely we would have been happy with something just a bit better and bigger than where we were. Grateful of any improvement on circumstances. Now the angels were telling us to describe exactly what we wanted as if money was not an issue. No holding back. Life had taught me well... And here is what I wrote.

My wish list...

1. A three bedroom house with a garden big enough to fit Anisha's trampoline.

2. Smallest bedroom to be a decent size still.

3. Separate living room and dining room space

4. A nice décor to our taste, ready to move into so we didn't have to decorate

5. A good sized kitchen with a big window looking out onto the garden, where the kitchen sink is, so I can watch Anisha play whilst stood doing the pots.

6. Nice big patio doors at the back so I can easily wheel our bird cage in and out when nice weather.

7. A big porch to walk into from the street, so that when walking the dogs there was space to clean them up before bringing them into the house. Space also to have cupboards in

the porch to keep all the dogs stuff and our gloves and sunglasses etc.
8. Plenty of storage space, like a garage?
9. That the house is in a nice area and in walking distance to Anisha's school.
10. A nice bathroom.
11. A nice new car.

We were told to put these lists on a wall, somewhere we could see them every day. The angels told us that this would reinforce our dreams by giving them attention every day, enticing them quicker into our realities. We did just that, until the day we moved house, displaying them on our living room wall, amongst Anisha's drawings. Within four months of creating these lists, I had the sudden urge to start looking for houses to move into. I began searching what was out there for rent. Christian kept telling me I was mad, as we still didn't have a penny towards our deposit. I felt persistent on looking for a three bedroom house, knowing that I would find one, much cheaper than what it was worth. I wasn't ready to compromise. Despite the houses being much more expensive in the area close to my daughter's school, that's the area I continued to look.

Everyone thought I was mad and just wasting my time. Especially when I went as far as dragging Christian along to a couple of houses to view. The two we viewed just didn't seem right. The one Anisha and I went to view alone was the one we both really liked, though there were viewable improvements to be made, I looked beyond the illusion. I gathered that it was these needed improvements that bought the cost of the monthly rent down so much. I had to wait until the Monday to ring the estate agents to put in our interest. On doing so I was told that three other families had expressed an interest in the house and that the agents now had to leave it in the hands of the landlord to decide which family he would prefer to move in.

Well that was it! I thought... We had not ever met this man, but what sane landlord would accept the family with a child and two dogs? The lady at the agency said herself that she thought our chances were slim, but we just had to wait to see what the landlord decided. I waited all day for an answer... And the answer was "YES!" The next step was to put a £300 holding fee down to pay administration fees for background checks. My dad was able to help with £250 and I managed the rest. My daddy tried desperately to talk me out of it as he just couldn't fathom where I was going to get the rest of the money from for the deposit and first month's rent. To be honest neither did I at this point. I just knew everything was going to work out, somehow. My dad was also worried that we would lose the admin and holding fee if we didn't get accepted. I was fully aware this was a big risk we were taking, but put my absolute trust in the angels that I was doing right.

I let Christian know the great news when he got home from work. After getting over initial panic and shock at what I had done, he put his faith in me and his trust in the angels. After a few days Christian asked me, that if we were accepted and they needed the deposit, where were we going to get it from? I admitted I didn't know with a smile, but again reassured him, as the angels did me, that everything would be fine. A couple of days later to that Christian made his final payment for the finance of his car that he'd had the last three years. On this day the angels smiled at me and said "And this is where your money will come from." I told Christian that if we were lucky enough to get accepted for this house, he would have to sell his car immediately for us to raise the deposit. He wasn't best pleased, but agreed that if that is what needed doing, he would do it. However he felt sure he would be lucky to get £600 for it. Nowhere near enough for the deposit.

That day came with the news that we had been accepted! I rang Christian straight away to tell him he was to go to the garage I told him to go to and sell his car to them. I felt adamant that it had to be this particular garage not too far from us. He sold his car, raising the exact amount needed for our deposit. We then had four weeks to save up the first month's rent, which was plenty of time. One week before moving in we had to go to the estate agents and pay the rest of the monies and sign all the documents. On doing so Christian and I asked if the lady could ring the landlord and ask if he would mind us repainting the house and having the beautiful flooring re-buffed and coated. We said we were happy to pay for these changes and do the work ourselves. We asked only that he could have the upstairs carpets shampooed.

The next day the lady from the agency rang us saying the landlord was enquiring on what colours we wanted where. I told her so that she could pass on the message. A couple of hours later she rang again to inform us the landlord was carrying out all the work we wanted doing himself, so that it would be ready for us to move in on the day we had planned.

I couldn't believe our luck! I thought this was the reason we were getting away with such a cheap rent in comparison to other homes for rent in that area. Now there was no other reason than that we had fallen incredibly lucky.

The day we picked up the keys for the house and stepped inside we were blown away. It was beautiful and freshly decorated. The Parquet flooring looked amazing and gleamed! I was so overwhelmed, feeling worried to wake up from this perfect dream. As a quick move we piled everything into the garage and pulled boxes out, one by one to unpack. About three weeks later most of it was done, just odd boxes of bits and pieces to slot in. It was like Christmas! We had so much stuff that had been wrapped up and kept away in storage for two years, which we forgot we even had! Then I came across one box with all the papers and drawings I had quickly taken down off the wall from the flat. I found mine and Christian's wish lists.

As I read through each wish I realised every single one had come true. It took this for me to realise the elements of the house that fulfilled each criteria. We had a big porch which we had put cupboards and drawers in, a beautiful and nice sized garden, kitchen sink looking out to the garden, a nice bathroom, separate living room and dining space with a dining table... And I sat reading this list in the smallest bedroom of the house, which wasn't that small. We were in a very picturesque location just a ten minute walk from my daughter's school. The only thing we hadn't got at that time was the new car... However a year on, as I sit here writing this chapter, we just got our brand new car. The funniest thing is every morning when I would drive down this road to take my daughter to school I would look at the gorgeous pink house there and say "One day we're going to live there, I love that house!" Well we were close enough... We live just over the road from that house and I get to look at it every day from our bedroom windows. Happy days.

One of Christian's biggest concerns was keeping up payments for all the bills and rent. The same weekend of us moving house I got an interview at my daughter's school for a teaching assistant position. After a week of being in our new house I heard I had got the job! Everything seemed to be coming at once. Now we knew everything would be alright and to top it off. I got a job doing what I loved best. Working with children again. The hours were perfect so I didn't have to worry about childcare for Anisha and it didn't take extra time from us being together.

Despite living the dream, I got to a point where I just didn't have the time I'd had before to dedicate to spirit, to the angels, or meditations. I could occasionally fit in odd readings on an evening, but that was it. I was too busy to listen to what they had to tell me most of the time, so they began finding other ways of getting to me again. When I did capture odd opportunities at a weekend to meditate, there would be urges to give more of myself to them and they began to show me aspects of my life that were not being fulfilled by the work I was doing. They wanted me working elsewhere, on a bigger scale where my help could reach out to more. My knowledge needed sharing with the world. They wanted me to teach, guide and inspire others. They wanted me have time to meditate more for myself to develop my own spiritual progression and in turn develop others. To be honest, I thought this was a big ask. I just didn't feel up to the job! Me? Felt like a lot of responsibility. I just about got by looking after myself and my own little family.

They pointed out to me, that since moving house and starting work, I had not added any more to my book and that it was important for this book to get out there! They showed me more books in the future I am to write and other work they saw me doing. Some of it very exciting I must say, though at the time it seemed so unlikely! However, I had learned to trust. I began to feel torn. I loved being in a wonderful work environment where all the staff were so sweet, pleasant and supportive of one another. I loved being around the beautiful energy of the children. I liked having the security of a regular extra income, which also helped to pay for treats we couldn't previously afford.

I was beginning to feel and see spirit energies more and more at school, finding it hard to block them out. My own unused energy was beginning to cause chaos too. On a couple of occasions I had gone into the staff room and within minutes the clock would start to go crazy. Both hands just spinning! Then I'd be on medical room duty and you could guarantee the clock would also go mad. There were so many children's name to remember from the whole school, especially on playground duty. I had the worst memory, but this is where spirit would help me. I hated forgetting their names as didn't want them to feel they didn't matter to me and that I didn't care enough to remember. They helped me a lot in fact.

It was beautiful to see different spirit energies of previous teachers working with the children. Teachers that had long passed away. I would watch a child in year two seeming confused with his maths work. His head held in one hand and the pencil motionless in the other. I could see a spirit working with him. Sending thoughts to his little mind helping him to understand the work he was to do... Then I would look again. He'd got it! There was no stopping him as his pencil whizzed away writing down all the answers. Other times I would see some of the children's guardian angels open up to me. I did not ask for these occurrences, they just happened. I was very sensitive to picking up on the children's emotions, needs and times they were not quite themselves.

As I helped out in one class, one of the girls didn't seem herself and I instinctually knew to tread extra careful with her that day. Not out of fear, just by being aware she might be easily upset. It was her turn to come out and read with me in a quiet corner. As she read, her guardian angel opened up to me and said that she'd had nightmares during the night, which then kept her awake for some time. It was for that reason she wasn't herself today. Once she finished reading she rubbed her tired eyes and gave a big yawn.

"My goodness you seem tired today!" I said to her smiling.

"Yes!" She replied. "I had bad dreams last night and couldn't get back to sleep."

"Oh dear." I replied. "I am sorry to hear that. I hope you manage to sleep better tonight." As she left me I sent out a quick prayer to Arch Angel Michael asking that he take her fear away tonight and help her to sleep easy. I also asked for her to be given strength to help her through the rest of the day. As I sent out the prayer he appeared behind the girl. As he walked away with her he nodded and smiled, reassuring me my requests were being heard. I saw her half hour later, bright as a button, bouncing around in the playground.

One particular day during staff training, the most beautiful and powerful guardian angels opened up to me, of a lady who had come to us to give training. As she presented her work with her lovely upbeat energy, I admired her enthusiasm to the work she did. The angels opened up to me to let me know she needed help. Someone to talk to. They told me she would be very interested in the work I do with the angels and would really benefit from a reading. They told me that behind all those smiles laid a broken heart. I was instantly connected to her energy and saw and felt all that she did. I then admired her even more for how she coped and still came across to others.

There was nothing I could do with this information given to me. It would have been incredibly unprofessional for me to have approached this lovely lady at work about all of this. Instead I tried to capture odd moments with her through the day, offering her food or drinks from the staff room etc. This moment was a massive eye opener for me. I know now that the angels of this lady opened up for me to see my path more clearly. I felt helpless and restricted. Confined within the rules of the workplace I was. I had to conform, respect rules and boundaries and be careful of what I said and to who, just in case I got myself into trouble, lording what they might think to be religious beliefs etc. I couldn't do it anymore. I was shown the light. I was shown that I needed my freedom to speak, my freedom to work in helping others without limitation. I needed not to walk in fear of others reactions or opinions. I needed to be me... And THIS was me... I AM me The angels reassured me that I would be fine and that my family would still be looked after financially. I put my full faith in them, trusted completely and handed my notice in the following week.

There have been times since then that we have really struggled. However, even when its last minute... The angel's miracles always shine through. My family and I haven't gone without. We have been kept safe, fed and still live in our beautiful home, where I deliver much of my work from now.

Chapter 23

I Choose To Be Happy

No matter what any of us ever go through, we have a choice as to how we are going to let our pasts affect us. Some might spit upon this very sentence. However YOU are the only ones that have control over your own life. This might take a lot of mental strength, but it is strength we all hold. The power of our thoughts are immense. Our mind is the overall controller of our entire being on this earth. Our wisdom, knowledge and spirit is how we control our minds. There has been plenty of research over the years to provide strong correlations and evidence that mental stress affects our health, to the extremes of incurring cancerous conditions. An imbalance of stressor hormones can bring on depressive side effects, which depression in itself can bring on a whole range of mental and physical symptoms. External stress or and life situations we are going through at that time are enough to create this hormonal imbalance internally.

As a nation, the human race is renowned for passing the buck, placing blame and passing on the responsibility to another. A piece of psychological research that explains this phenomena perfectly is the evidence sought from the Milgrim Study (1963). I won't go into detail on that, but you can Google or find the information yourself if you are interested. I warn you though... it is both mind blowing and disturbing to read. Reading into this study helps us to also understand Nazi Soldiers under the reign of Hitler and the mentality behind your everyday human beings, committing such vile acts to another, on such a grand scale. It is in fact our entire responsibility to assess ourselves and our own actions. It is our personal responsibility to how we allow ourselves to act, behave, speak or even dwell on past and present reactions.

We are fantastic and incredibly intelligent creatures to give understanding to how and why we may have reacted to a situation, or what the reasoning is behind it. However there is a difference to gaining understanding, to giving excuses. Some people may interpret the knowledge that explains "Why?" to actually giving an excuse to their present behaviours and beings. I know... I've been there. This is all part of the journey into growing and developing and becoming stronger. Sometimes we act out as an excuse... "I've had such a hard week! I'm getting slaughtered at the weekend to get over it!" Some more excuses.

"My last boyfriend cheated on me. I won't trust any man again!"

"It's not my fault! Can you blame me?! She was flaunting it in my face!"

"What does she expect going out dressed like that?"

"She pushed me to the edge! She knows what I can be like! She wouldn't stop! She made me hit her!"

"Well all my friends were doing it, so I did."

"It's not my fault she's over sensitive."

"But what chance did I have of a normal life? I was abused as a child."

"I came from a family of drug addicts and thieves. I was gonna end up the same regardless."

This list could go on and on and on and on... And though each comment may hold some truth, the biggest truth which is apparent to anyone reading these things is that there was a soul terrorist. Another that terrorised in some way, someone else's soul... Or at least tried... Fact... But the so called victims? Now the power has been handed over... What are YOU going to do with it? Are you going to allow that negative energy, that abuse, that anger of another's flow through you and your future days? Or are you going to work on transmuting that negative energy, that selfishness of another... Into love and positivity... "How?" you might ask... "Ridiculous!" some might say! Especially counsellors! I don't want to go putting anyone out of business, but I'm aware I'm not doing you any favours right now.

The "How's?"... They lie with you. We all handle drama in different ways. How long we allow those dramas to affect us truly is in your hands. How we let those dramas affect us is in your own power. It is good to have a knowledge and understanding of others behaviours, or how we might be left feeling after certain events have taken place. But this knowledge is not to feed excuses... It is to open our eyes and to see with compassion, with understanding and with love. We don't have to agree with someone else's bad choices, we don't have to go along with it... to understand it in some form however, gives you the world of power... Because with that power... You cannot be defeated... You can no longer be hurt... You are forever protected.

There is that saying... "What doesn't kill us makes us stronger." This is a powerful statement to have been made and is the very grounding to our Earthly existence. We may wonder through life never having experienced financial issues, rape, child abuse, domestic violence, school bullies etc... What some might call quite a blessed lifetime. Though we all at some level and at some point go through our hard times. We may not think or feel it at the time, but it truly is those times that give us the most profound learning of ourselves and others. It is those times that put us to the test... How we allow ourselves to react to them. We are faced with tests on a daily basis. When our children play up, when the husband comes home in a strop, when someone cuts us up on the motorway, when someone passes a comment of judgement upon you or your family.

These tests are not put there being judged by another, or from God... They are to test our own strength. No one holds the right to judge you and God and the Angels absolutely do not judge... The only judge of character allowed is that of yourself... and even then... If we see through the eyes of the angels, with complete compassion and understanding, we can quickly learn to forgive ourselves of our mistakes and move forwards with love. If it were not for some difficult times, how could we ever learn to appreciate the good to its fullest?

The good that we are continually surrounded by? We just don't always see it.

Some say that the Earth and lives lived upon it, are a school of learning. Valuable learning that can be taken with us onto the next level. I believe this one hundred percent. I was not born saintly. I experienced many things in life that made me bitter for some time, angry and act in unruly ways... I allowed those things to bring out the worst in me... But I experienced it... And with that experience I have learned. I have experienced many heartaches in life, been physically and mentally abused, yet today I walk with a smile on my face. I am full of kind words to pass onto another, I am full of hope and optimism for the future. The smile I carry is not a cover up of how I really feel. It is my true feelings. It is a sign of my strength and a sign of my true happiness.

For children that are born into families full of rejection, abuse, torment and anger. The families themselves have to take full responsibility for their own actions, but the children are the innocent, despite how they cope and deal with the situations. They are the innocent because truly at that point they do not hold power... They cannot choose what they can and can't do, nor can they remove themselves from situations and people that are causing them pain. On this Earth and still to this day, children do not have rights. They are the needy and the only ones with right to be needy, as they rely upon the adults for everything, for survival. Each child without disability, gets to an age where survival can be dealt with. Basic needs can be provided for... By the self.

It is around this point that we truly can start to take responsibility for our lives and our actions. Step by step as the days go on we gain more power. The power to learn, to develop, to make the right choices. We gain independence with each passing day. Taking ourselves to school, shopping alone with friends, going on nights out, learning to drive, studying, getting a job, saving, and moving away from home. Suddenly the power is in our hands. How we deal with this power, with this gained independence is up to us. How our lives pan out and end up as an adult, is our making... no one else's.

At this point the angels have asked me to point out the Celebration of the Bat Mitzvah in the religion of Judaism. This celebration takes place for boys at the age of thirteen years old and is to celebrate the child coming into adulthood, where they are now seen as equal to adults, taking on responsibility for their actions and certain situations. In Jewish law they are no longer seen as a minor. For girls the celebrations take place at the age of twelve. From this day they are given a blessing a week from the Torah, for them to learn and fully absorb it into their very being and lifestyle. They are now obligated to observe the commandments and teachings of the Torah. I have to say I knew nothing about this until the angels asked me to mention it in my book. Having researched it now, I see why.

At times we have to face the consequence of another's actions. Being made redundant for example. Again it is up to us how we deal with the situation. Do you go into panic? Allow your life to go downhill and blame everyone else for it? Or do you see it as a turning point in your life? A chance for something new? Something better possibly? You might get into another job which does not pay as well... but it's a job and means of survival. You might have to face the situation by selling your bigger home and settling for something smaller. You may not afford the holidays as often or even at all. Do you dwell on what was? Or do you find the hidden qualities in life and appreciate what you do have? The simple pleasures in life that cost nothing? Being thankful for the experiences you have had. Having being in a position with money, living up to a certain lifestyle, these changes can be understandably difficult at first, but once you realise the true importance of life... All the things on a materialistic level become irrelevant and true happiness can be gained. Do you choose to dwell on the past? Or do you choose to embrace the here and now! Allowing yourself to move forwards and to grow.

I mentioned earlier in my book about not allowing myself to be the victim, having had to face certain situations in life. I refused to live up to the stereotype of what people thought these victims to be. I did not handle this in the best of ways at the time, but it has taken my journey in life up until now to handle it more positively. I understand now that I did not do anything wrong or deserving of the things inflicted upon me by another. I understand that the selfish ways of the others are part of their journeys in life and a part of their learning. I am not angry or act in ways of self-pity or self-destruction. I have forgiven myself of wrong choices made, as a result to these situations. I am not a victim, I am victorious to this day of all I have had to face... And why? Because I choose to be happy.

Chapter 24

The Here and Now!

So here I am now. Whole and at one with the self... Most of the time. That's just it. We live in hope of this perfect life. However life will never cease to test us. It is these tests that make us stronger, wiser and understanding. Life cannot be an endless path of bliss, for how would we appreciate the small things, the good times and laughter, if life was always this way? It is those hard times that make us appreciate more than ever, the simple things in life. It's OK to fall. It's how quick we learn to get back up that is important. All of the tests we pass, we activate another element within our own light. The Master St Germaine, from higher realms of spirit came to me in meditation to explain this phenomena. Imagine all around you is a ball of light, however most of the light is shadowed with a greyish tint. Every time you conquer, master or achieve within everyday life, you activate another speckle within the grey area of your light.

Eventually your light becomes fully activated with no grey tinge and your light becomes whole. It is at this point, or even close to this point, that we feel whole, complete, at peace and happy within our own space. You see? You are the light. The more of us on the Earth that activate their light codes to that wholeness, they merge with one another's, creating that oneness amongst man, amongst life and all creation as we know it. You merge completely into the elements of the universe and become one with all that is. Having mastered the self, your abilities merge to higher frequencies and your potential truly does become limitless. You can enter into the realms of the angels, the heavens, past life realms, future realms and the realms of the elementals. The universe is the source of all energy. The more we become the source of all that is, we are able to tap into every aspect and potential that the universe holds. WE ARE THE UNIVERSE.

There are energies within our universe we can call upon at any time, to cater for every need. If you feel tired and heavy and need a burst of energy to get you through the rest of the day? Instead of reaching for that second, third or fourth coffee of the day, ask. Ask the universe, call upon the angels, and breathe in that given energy free of charge and endless in supply. Try calling direct upon Arch Angel Raphael for energy, for soothing and releasing of pressure and headaches in your head. Pains in your body and relief of stressor energy that does not serve, nor help you in life. Ask... And I am given a promise from the angels, that if you have got this far in my book, absorbed all the lessons it has given and wisdoms it has shared, then truly you will receive all that you ask for. That promise is not given from a well of my own ego, but to those that believe, to those that trust and to those that carry the faith in their hearts, that all is possible.

Start looking out for the signs that your loved ones are around you. That the angels watch over you and guide your way... If you choose to listen. It is possible to live in this higher state of consciousness, with a more blissful awareness of all the beauty that surrounds us, whilst our feet still touch upon the Earth. It is a gift that only you are capable of giving to yourself. There are workshops, classes and others you can go to for help and guidance, but only you can make the real changes in your own life and start to grow into your true self and walk that path of bliss, the spiritual path to the higher. We begin to see the world from a different perspective and understand people on deeper levels. Acceptance is the key! Do not take everything in life personally or allow people or situations to offend you. Accept others for their differences and do not allow others opinions to govern your own life. Do what makes you happy. The right people will always remain in your life. Learn to let go of those that do not serve their purpose in your life anymore. Those that interfere with your road to happiness, or try to hold you back in any way.

Remember that we are all on this Earth to learn different lessons for our soul progression. We are all on different roads that lead to the same highway. We are all just going at different paces and some are a little further from the highway than others. Never be afraid to share your wisdom, your knowledge of all that the eyes do not see, for you could be that road sign on someone else's journey that helps them on their way, reassures them they are on the right path. Learn to listen to your heart more and not the ego that instils the fear, causing the brain to react in survival mode with logical explanations as to why you shouldn't do something. It is this fear based ego that holds most of us back from our dreams and our true purpose in life. Let it go. Be brave and have trust that you are not alone. You have all the help in the universe waiting for you to ask. To ask, so that it can give. You have the universe behind you, supporting you... So go live your dreams! Be happy.

If we can detach from the illusions that our reality appears to be, we can detach from the trauma and direct stress of that we are experiencing. By detaching we can re-assess from a different perspective. When harbouring hurt or stress from situations it causes us to react irrationally or in ways that do not serve our, or others greater good. This is where meditation can be your most powerful tool. Meditation can be used for self-reflection, calming of the mind, connecting with higher sources and all round better wellbeing. In meditation we can take ourselves on the most amazing journeys to where ever we want to be. You can astral travel into the galaxy and far beyond. All in the search for wisdom, for knowledge, for soul awakenings leading you to your higher self, your whole self. Discover who you really are and get in tuned with the higher you that knows truly who you are. It's all possible... And trust me, so worth it.

When I talked earlier about the tests that pass to activate another element of our own light? Well these tests do not have to be big or traumatic. It can be a friend that is need of a helping hand or shoulder to cry on. Do you offer that shoulder or tell them you're too busy? Do you really care?

Have you taken the time to see life from his or hers life right now? What they are going through. It might be your child kicking up a fuss and tantrum about something or other. Do you scream and shout in return? Or do you choose to get down to their level, remain calm and try to understand from their stance? Have you had the morning from hell and everything that could go wrong, went wrong? Do you act snappy and miserable with everyone else that comes into your path for the rest of the day, sharing your misery and probably risking others to feel miserable too? Or do you find that inner strength to rise above the trauma. Breathe it out, letting go of the past and responding with a smile and cheer to others around you? Possibly uplifting them from a rotten time of it, of late. You see? Many may walk around with a smile, or getting on in their car on their journey. You don't know what that other person has been through. A smile can hide a thousand frowns. Always be kind. Those wise choices to be made alone, choices from your hearts well of compassion, are those that activate our codes, our elements into reaching that higher state of consciousness... In becoming your light and becoming whole.

The tests that we face in life are not set by any higher source, or from God. They are put in our lives by life itself. Every step we take, every time we say or do anything in life, is a test. A test to how we respond, how we allow it to make us feel, are we quick to place blame or do we accept responsibility for our own role in the matter? Do we seek to understand or do we just label others and other groups of society for appears to lie on the surface? Are we quick to judge? Or do we understand there may be many other aspects that have led to a certain outcome? For all we have to face in life, we are tested. Do we make or break We decide. You are the keeper of your own soul, your own destiny. Keep it well. We are all equal and in the eyes of the angels, all deserving of the best in life. See yourself through the eyes of the angels and see that you too are worth the best that life can give.

So many of us walk through this life with their eyes closed. Throughout life we have all experienced many, what can be perceived as coincidences. It's time to open your eyes. To see those all too many coincidences as the true blessings received. To see that life as we know it, consists of so much more than our shadowed eyes have been allowed to see. Things are working on much higher frequencies than we can understand. How many times have you thought of a friend or family, or gone to ring them, then they have called you? Or you were thinking of someone from the past and they make an appearance or get in contact a few days or weeks later. These are examples that everything is linked, that the universe is a part of you and everyone and thing as you know it. We all hold some sorts of psychic ability, but are unaware how to tune into them and develop them. We are all beings of limitless potential. Learn to use all you have been gifted with.

The world we live today is made up of sound waves, electrical waves, sonic waves, radio waves and mobile phone waves that make our phones ring wherever we are. These are all waves and vibrations that we know exist, but cannot see. The waves of our own energy immerse into the universe the same way. The waves of spirit and angels work again in the same way. They are all working on vibrations, frequencies and invisible waves. We know this to be true in our hearts. It is only the mind and logical solving that will tell you different. The logic and mind that is fuelled by the ego and not the heart. It is the ego that creates us to be afraid of all that is not fully understood. It is the ego especially that needs control over all it knows, to create that feeling of security. Is it not that same ego that created a society of slavery and savage ruling? Why do we fight that that is most natural? Start opening your eyes to the truths of reality. Open your arms to receiving and embrace all the help, guidance and gifts that are offered to you day in and day out.

Every time you see a feather in a random place, find money, find that thing you've been looking for! Every time you realise yet another beautiful coincidence that has worked in your favour. Give a smile and thanks to the heavens. Give appreciation to the universe and show your gratitude... Simply by allowing the occurrence to warm your heart, knowing it is more than coincidence. This is the universe working with you, bringing you signs to uplift and remind you you're never alone. The vibrations your energy sends out to the universe at that moment, is all it needs in return.

I love how the sciences that have taught society all these years, are now beginning to find scientific evidence supporting what people like myself have been stating for years. Though I myself do not need science to prove any such phenomena to make it my belief, there are many out there that do... And for those people who still have not learnt to trust their hearts... These sciences are a wonderful gift of man. There is so much to read up on and documentaries to watch, supporting these theories of different dimensional living and workings going on within different frequencies etc. Google is a wonderful tool! There is a great documentary called the Cosmos: A Spacetime Odyssey. It is for you to educate yourself on these topics, to determine how deep you wish to understand all that is.

I took the big leap of faith in leaving my full time employment, to doing this work solely. Since then, times have been hard, but we got through it. The patience and continued faith has pulled me through and I am now in a better place financially and all around. I myself am still embarking an incredible learning journey, every day is something new. I now run classes enlightening spiritual awareness and I run different workshops to help others with their spiritual work. I give different types of readings to people from spirit, the angels, masters and all different light energies of the universe. I aid people in delving into past lifetimes, in order to help them along in this lifetime. I absolutely love my work with the angels. Out of all the different therapies learned from my studies, I have not yet come across one better or more effective than the therapy given by the angels. They are the wisest and powerful beings to help guide our way, to help shine lights of understanding on topics and situations we never thought possible... And ultimately, they bring their pure love and compassion which is felt with their presence.

I cannot thank my wonderful husband enough, who has supported me through every step of this journey. Despite some of my decisions being drastic and possibly threatening to us all, he put his faith in me. I took that faith and persisted through all the hard times. Planting his faith deep within my heart and feeding into it every day, so that it blossoms so beautifully now. I see an end drawing on those difficult times of our life... And so begins a new chapter...

The illustration on the front cover of my book was a gift from my husband for my thirtieth birthday. It was at this time we left our lovely flat to stay for what was meant to be a short stay in the small flat we ended up in for two years. We had no money and couldn't afford to do anything special, so this was his gift. He is a truly talented artist and little did he know at the time, a wonderful psychic artist too. From a holiday taken to Cairo in Egypt for my daddy's sixtieth birthday, I was in awe of the ancient Egyptian Goddess Isis. I adored everything she stood for and all she symbolised. She is the goddess of the faithful wife and doting mother. She symbolises pure love in its truest forms. She is beauty and fertility. She is the warrior strength of the femininity.

It is of recent times I have discovered my true and very personal connections with this beautiful goddess, having had certain past lives made so apparent to me. Unknowing of this nearly three years ago, my Christian drew me as the Sun goddess, Isis, encasing my true love, him. This picture was drawn out of love and a depiction of true love. It felt right to use this as the front cover of my book, for truly I have survived this life up till yet and love survived each hardship, each battle and conquered all that tried to diminish it from within me. I am "A Survivor of Love" and so too are each and every one of you that have suffered ventures big or small and are still here to tell your story. You are still here with love in your heart and a smile on your face. Understand that there is no vibration stronger than love and that truly, love can conquer anything. It is not weak to be soft hearted and show your love for others. In the world that we live today, it is the strongest and bravest thing you can do and be as a human being... Love. The picture on the front cover holds many secrets... All to be told in the following book.

I thank you all from my heart, for taking the time to read my book and I live in hope that somehow, the words have helped you in your personal life journey. My book to follow will be a continuation of many more teachings and wisdoms from the higher, with a few more uplifting stories to be shared. I wish you all a magical journey in this lifetime and beyond. Angel blessings to you xxx